D1219340

SATURN V
The Moon Rocket

From the first rockets in ancient China, to the brilliant pioneering work of the American Robert Goddard, to the terrifying German V-bombs of World War II, knowledge of rocket power slowly grew. Today rocketry has moved to the center of the scientific stage, and the United States has undertaken an immense project—to land two astronauts on the moon before 1970. Thousands of technicians and engineers across the country are involved in this monumental task, known as Project Apollo. Described are the Mercury, Gemeni and current Apollo manned spacecraft . . . the Viking, Thor, Jupiter, Redstone and Saturn I rockets . . . the vast network of factories, transportation facilities, testing grounds, launch pads and tracking systems developed to support the space program . . . and, finally, the Saturn V rocket that soon will power a manned Apollo spacecraft to the moon.

SATURN V

illustrations by **MARTHA SHIELDS**

photographs

JULIAN MESSNER

THE
MOON
ROCKET

by WILLIAM G. HOLDER

Edited by GLENN HOLDER

New York

Published simultaneously in the United States and Canada by
Julian Messner, a division of Simon & Schuster, Inc.,
1 West 39 Street, New York, N.Y. 10018. All rights reserved.

Printed in the United States of America

SBN 671-32121-8 Cloth Trade
671-32122-6 MCE

Library of Congress Catalog Card No. 69-13045

Dedicated to
Virgil I. Grissom,
Edward H. White and
Roger B. Chaffee, who made the
greatest sacrifice in America's
race to the moon.

Acknowledgments

The author is indebted to several of his associates for their review and suggestions—Frank Swortzel, George Gerhard, Joseph Ainsworth, James Sisk and Cameron Deen. Also deserving great thanks are the many different centers of the National Aeronautics and Space Administration without whose assistance this book would have not have been possible. Valuable help was also provided by Rocketdyne, North American Rockwell and McDonnell Douglas Companies. Special thanks go to Billy Neighbors, Marshall Space Flight Center, and to Willis Robinson, Boeing Company, who taught me much about the Saturn. Also, thanks to Gail Roellig, who spent many hours typing the drafts, and last of all to my wife, Ruth Ann, who aided in the typing and helped push the book to completion with her encouragement.

Contents

1

The Mystery
of the Moon

The morning of November 9, 1967, at Launch Complex 39A, Cape Kennedy, Florida, was cloudy, but the weatherman had reported that clear weather was on the way. This good news added to the excitement and suspense that were already present everywhere in the Cape area.

The reason for the excitement was easy to observe from outside the restricted launch area, for in the distance could be seen a massive silver rocket poised for a leap into space. On the side of the rocket gleamed the initials "U.S.A." in bright red colors.

Work by thousands of technicians and engineers for many months had brought the United States to this day. Bringing a rocket of this size to the launch position was a tremendous task in itself. The rocket, after being shipped to Cape Kennedy, had been assembled in the huge Vehicle Assembly Building nearby. This 525-foot-high building contains the necessary lifting devices for mating the stages and spacecraft into the complete rocket. After the assembly operations had been completed, the rocket was placed on a tracked transporter and moved with its mobile launcher to the launch pad. In its three-and-one-half-mile trip from the Vehicle Assembly Building to the launch pad, the transporter had carried more than 11,000,000 pounds!

The countdown had proceeded smoothly through all of the

many complex check-out operations. Four and one-half million pounds of liquid oxygen (lox) and rocket fuel had already been pumped into the first stage, and the two upper stages had been filled with more than 1,000,000 pounds of lox and liquid hydrogen.

All was in readiness for the first launch of the world's most powerful rocket—the Saturn V. This first launch was to test the rocket's structure and the heat shield of the Apollo spacecraft. Then, if all went well, the spacecraft would be driven back to earth at 25,000 miles per hour following a two-orbit mission.

As the countdown neared zero, every person in the enormous crowd of spectators listened intently as a loudspeaker blared out the progress of the prelaunch preparations. The nearby beaches were also viewing positions for thousands of other rocket enthusiasts. Many of these watchers had seen numerous earlier launches, but the great size of the Saturn V was providing the greatest thrill yet. Within the launch control center an army of technicians bent forward, intently scanning their consoles for the tiniest hint of trouble. There was no trouble to be found.

The Saturn V consists of thousands of parts which must work together. A failure of any part could keep the rocket from accomplishing its mission. It is important, therefore, to monitor the many internal functions both before and during the launch. If a malfunction does occur, the problem can be pinpointed and changes made to prevent it from happening again on future flights. The technique of monitoring rocket functions is known as telemetry. So great is the amount of telemetric data acquired from a single launch that it requires weeks after the flight to evaluate it fully.

he first Saturn V launch vehicle lifts off its pad at Launch Complex 39A on No-
ember 9, 1967.

The man at the loudspeaker, in a tone of serious suspense, continued, "Thirty seconds and counting!" Countless cameras were raised into position to record whatever might happen— a successful launch, a failure or perhaps an explosion of almost indescribable force. A vast tracking network situated down the Eastern Test Range waited to record the events during the rocket's expected trajectory. A large recovery force was poised in the Pacific to recover the Apollo spacecraft in its plunge from space.

"Ten! Nine! Eight! Seven! Ignition sequence started!" came the words from the loudspeaker. Suddenly a large white cloud poured from the base of the rocket as the vast power of the five first-stage rocket engines was brought to life. Startled by the noise, a flock of wild geese flapping across the cloudy sky suddenly broke their V formation. Air pressure waves generated by the belching rocket slapped at the spectators seated in an open grandstand.

"Six! Five! Four! Three! Two! One!—Lift off!" Slowly, as though a great hand were trying to hold it back, the Saturn V began to rise. Spewing a billowing trail of flame, the 6,000,-000-pound rocket finally cleared the top of the launch tower and rose skyward. Gulping more than 15 tons of fuel a second, it began to gain speed, soon leaving the smoking and blackened launch pad far behind.

The 7,500,000 pounds of thrust produced by the first stage, which is called the S-IC stage, was one of the loudest sounds ever produced by man. The S-IC contained enough liquid oxygen to fill fifty-four railroad tank cars. The five first-stage engines produced as much power as eighty-five Hoover Dams. Each of the powerful pumps providing propellant to the engines could have emptied a 20,000-gallon swimming pool in less than half a minute. The fuel and oxidizer pumps for each engine were driven by a turbine producing the power of fifteen diesel locomotives.

Plaster fell from the roof of the launch control center, and crowd and technicians alike shouted, screamed and even cried for joy. Their "baby" was on its way, carrying the hope of their country in space. The Saturn V, as if acknowledging the human frenzy below, gracefully arched upward into the cloudy sky.

The lift-off weight of the Saturn V was more than 6,000,000 pounds, equal to the weight of twenty loaded jet airliners. More than 5,500,000 pounds of this total consisted of fuels for the propulsion systems of the three stages of the rocket. During the first-stage burn period, which lasted approximately two and one-half minutes, the rocket reached an altitude of 40 miles and could be seen 150 miles away. By this time, the first stage had burned out, and powerful retro-rockets separated it from the second stage. The 1,000,000-pound-thrust second stage, called the S-II stage, then ignited and drove the rocket to an altitude of more than 100 miles. During the second-stage burn period, the Apollo launch escape system was jettisoned. This system would be used in manned flights if it were necessary for the astronauts to escape during the early seconds of flight.

After the second stage was dropped off, the third stage, called the S-IVB, drove itself and the Apollo payload into a near circular orbit, the entire package weighing 140 tons. This was almost five times the previous weight of a single launch put into orbit by the United States. During the third orbit of its mission, the S-IVB ignited again and drove the rocket into a new orbit with an apogee (highest altitude of an orbit) of more than 11,000 miles. The S-IVB then dropped off and an engine on the spacecraft fired, driving the Apollo spacecraft back toward the earth at 25,000 miles per hour. This is the lunar reentry speed the Apollo capsule will experience if all goes well when it attempts to bring men back from the moon.

Although heated to more than 5000 degrees Fahrenheit, the Apollo survived its red-hot ride through the earth's atmosphere. Floated down by three parachutes, it landed in the Pacific Ocean, where it was immediately located and put on shipboard by the Pacific Recovery Force. The flight was an amazing success. The capsule settled into the water within sight of the main recovery ship.

Eight hours and thirty-seven minutes after the lift-off, the 12,000-pound heat-seared Apollo capsule was all that remained of the 6,000,000-pound Saturn V that had left Cape Kennedy the morning of that same day.

The radio and television broadcasters described the historic event as the successful beginning of the United States' effort to reach the moon. But was it really the beginning? Actually, the present Saturn V rocket is the result of dreams and theories of many great men down through the ages. Traveling to the moon has been one of man's great dreams for centuries, and now it appears his fancy will soon be realized.

For thousands of years man has observed the moon and other planets, and has wondered about their nature. He asked himself whether he would ever be able to travel to these worlds, places that, to the naked eye, seem so near on any clear night. Because of its seeming closeness to the earth, the moon has always had most of man's attention. The full moon on a clear night is a thing of beauty as well as of scientific interest, and it is understandable that man has always speculated about its nature. Then, too, there is the continually changing appearance of the moon from day to night, the fact that it gives light, the jagged appearance of its surface, and its effect on the ocean tides, all of which add to its mysteries.

Since man, down through the ages, has always desired to leave the earth on which he is so firmly implanted, great thinkers have from time to time proposed ways to accomplish this monumental task. To realize how long man has had the desire to visit other planets in the universe, one need merely turn to the space theories of the ancient Greeks. They believed that the earth was the center of the universe, with all other heavenly bodies revolving about it. Then, about 300 B.C., Aristarchus of Samos reasoned that the sun was fixed and that the planets revolved around it. This theory was much too advanced for its time, however, and it was rejected by most ancient Greek astronomers. Some 1800 years after Aristarchus had proposed the sun-centered theory, a Polish monk called Copernicus, for whom a moon crater has since been named, brought forth a similar theory, much of which is still accepted today.

The surface of the moon was strange to early viewers. Many superstitions and fears about the moon filled the hearts of early man. The moon gave them their first ideas of anything beyond this world and their first thoughts of outer space. The moon was for some time thought of as a mirror in which the image of the earth was reflected. Later, when primitive telescopes were developed, wise men imagined that the marks they saw on the moon were made by man.

We know today, however, that it would be impossible for

15

men to exist unprotected on the moon. A day and night on the moon would be equal to nearly an earth month. Fourteen earth days would be spent in intense heat, for the moon has no atmosphere to screen out the sun's rays. The other fourteen days would be spent in darkness and extreme cold.

It would be rewarding to the early astronomers if they could see that many of their theories have proved to be correct, and what has evolved from their early ideas. Of course, when these early space pioneers proposed their ideas, there were no rockets to test their theories. There were, however, many primitive attempts by man to conquer the air. Early Greek history tells of the inventor Daedalus, who constructed a pair of wings for his son to use in an attempt to escape from prison on the island of Crete near the southeast coast of Greece. But no one was able to devise a vehicle capable of continuous flight through the air until the late 1700's, when balloons filled with lighter-than-air gases were developed.

The Montgolfier brothers, Joseph and Jacques, sons of a wealthy French manufacturer, are credited with building, in 1783, the first airworthy balloon. The balloon, inflated by gases and hot air generated by burning straw, rose to an "astounding" altitude of 1000 feet. Interest in balloons continued throughout the nineteenth century, with hydrogen replacing the hot gas.

Balloons provided man with his first satisfactory, though limited, view of the earth. They also gave him a better opportunity to view and photograph the moon and other parts of the sky. Valuable information about the earth's atmosphere was also obtained from unmanned weather balloons. The world altitude record for a balloon was set in 1935, when a United

States Army balloon rose to an altitude of about fourteen miles. Until the arrival of rockets, balloons and ground-based telescopes provided man with all his knowledge of the moon and other planets.

Man could not learn much about the moon and other planets by using the planet earth as an example, for the surface record of the earth goes back only about 3,000,000,-000 years, which is about two-thirds the estimated age of the moon. Therefore, the beginning of the planet earth can only be guessed at and not scientifically investigated. Theories, however clever they may be, will never substitute for direct observations in shedding light on the origin of the moon and earth. Man must venture to the moon before he can determine how it all happened. And since we can now travel in space, it makes good sense that most of our scientific effort be directed toward the moon.

From the data obtained from the three unmanned NASA space programs, more has been learned in the last ten years about the moon than in all previous centuries. These moon programs are the hard-impact Ranger, the Lunar Orbiter and the soft-lander Surveyor. Data supplied by these programs have revealed that the moon is remarkably earthlike—the surface is gently rounded and rolling, and the soil is similar to that in our own yards and gardens.

The Ranger Program (1961–1965) consisted of nine launches, with the final three launches providing especially valuable facts about the moon. Launched by an Atlas-Agena rocket, the Ranger spacecraft was placed on a collision course with the moon. Once the spacecraft arrived within a certain distance of the moon, six powerful cameras began to photograph the surface until impact and finally destruction occurred.

The pictures the Ranger radioed back to earth showed for the first time the probability that the jagged appearance of much of the moon's surface could have been formed by volcanic eruption. There are craters of many different sizes and shapes.

Using photography from a moon orbit, the Lunar Orbiter is attempting to determine possible landing sites on the moon. The spacecraft, which weighs about 830 pounds, is launched from Cape Kennedy by an Atlas-Agena rocket. The Lunar Orbiter's camera system, with a visibility of 14,000 square miles of moon surface, points straight downward. Equipped with a special rocket engine, the spacecraft can change its orbit to photograph different parts of the moon's surface at an altitude of 575 nautical miles. So far the Orbiter has provided information on the moon's gravitational fields, on small meteors and on the back side and the polar regions of the moon.

The Surveyor program is our country's first attempt to soft-land a scientific package on the moon. The soft landing can determine whether the moon surface can support the weight of a spaceship carrying astronauts. Before Surveyor, it was quite generally believed that the moon's surface was covered by a layer of dust up to ten feet deep. Surveyor has proved, however, that there is no dust of any importance there and that the moon surface can easily support man when he arrives. Along with a camera system, the Surveyor carried a sampler for determining the structure of the lunar soil. The sampler, operated on earth command, conducted many tests and dug "lunar trenches." One might say that Surveyor I put man's eyes on the moon for the first time and that Surveyor III added a hand and an arm to the ship to make soil exploration possible.

The origin of the moon may be quite difficult to determine when astronauts finally set foot on its surface. The molten-textured rock probably will not be easy to classify. Another problem will be to determine whether the moon was created as a result of volcanic action or by a collision with a meteor. Analysis of moon soil would give us an approximate lunar age compared to the 4,500,000,000-year-old earth. Analysis of moon craters may provide information that will help us understand similar formations on the earth. Water erosion and vegetation down through the centuries have destroyed most of this type of evidence on the earth. The moon surface, however, has little or no water, wide temperature changes and a lack of oxygen, and is therefore unable to support any plant life. Probably the moon has changed very little since it was created.

Hopefully, then, when armed with lunar soil samples, man will finally be ready to solve the moon questions of the centuries: Was the moon "captured" by the earth's gravitational field, was it spun off from another planet, or was it created by a combining of gas and dust masses?

One day near the end of this decade an American astronaut will step out onto the surface of the moon. What he sees and does on this first mission will be the greatest adventure ever experienced by man. All previous discoveries about the moon, including those of the unmanned moon vehicles, will seem insignificant compared to this great accomplishment. From the earliest feeble beginnings with balloons to today's powerful rockets, man has been waiting hopefully and patiently for this day. Through the constant increase in man's mechanical capability, we now have the rocket to accomplish this monumental task—Saturn V: The Moon Rocket.

2

The Beginning

All of the accomplishments of the early rocket pioneers who made it possible for the United States to be where it is today in the field of rocketry are not known. Many of their meager successes were soon forgotten; only a few of their most important early accomplishments ever were recorded in writing or pictures. As is nearly always the case with anything radically new, many of the ideas of the fledgeling rocketeers were held up to scorn. They were just impractical dreamers, or more probably fools, said many who observed their work. However, it was from these humble beginnings that the massive Saturn V was born.

Although the first attempts at rocketry are unknown, the Chinese in the seventh century found that a mixture of charcoal, saltpeter and sulfur, or what is known today as gunpowder, would burn together at a high rate of speed. The Chinese also discovered that when this mixture was burned in a closed container, the exhaust gases that were produced would expand and destroy the container. They then learned to use this new source of power by attaching to an arrow a tube containing the mixture. The explosive mixture supplied to the arrow the world's first rocket power. Probably recognizing the great potential of what was called the "Arrow of Flying Fire" as a weapon of war, the Chinese are thought to have used it against their enemies.

One of the most interesting accounts of early Chinese

rocketry experiments describes the work of a Chinese gentleman called Wan-Hoo, who devised what he hoped would be a system of using rockets to propel a vehicle through the air. The device consisted of a chair to which were attached about fifty of the largest rockets he could find. Two kites were also attached to the chair to guide it back to earth after the rockets had burned out, if the experiment should work out as planned.

Thus, after all preparations were complete, the world's first rocket "countdown" started when Wan-Hoo positioned himself in the chair and was firmly strapped by his launch crew, consisting of about fifty helpers. Just how far Wan-Hoo intended to travel into space will never be known, but he had ideas on air travel that were many centuries ahead of his time. As the countdown approached zero, the helpers, rushing forward at Wan-Hoo's command, simultaneously lit the fifty rockets. The blast of flame and smoke that followed did indeed, according to the old story, resemble that which is produced by a modern rocket when the first stage engines are started. There was one important difference, however. The early space vehicle, namely Wan-Hoo and the chair, moved not that first inch. Once the smoke had cleared, all that remained of Wan-Hoo and the rocket chair was a smoldering pile of ashes. Unsuccessful as the attempt was, Wan-Hoo should probably be given his place in rocket history as the man who built and tested the first rocket-propelled vehicle.

Surprising as it may seem, the basic rocket idea discovered by the Chinese more than 1200 years ago is the same principle on which today's powerful solid-propellant rocket motors operate. The Chinese learned that the force produced by the burning gases was powerful and an important source of energy. That force was pushing equally on all parts of the rocket container. A good example of this is an inflated balloon. If the inside forces were not equal, the balloon would not retain its roundness. Now what happens if you release the balloon? It zooms crazily around until all the air inside is expended. The balloon moves in a direction opposite to that of the escaping gases. This movement is the result of an important scientific principle: the force pushing the balloon is exactly equal to that produced by the escaping gas. This equal force principle aptly illustrates Sir Isaac Newton's famous third law of motion—*for every action there is an opposite and equal reaction*. The force produced by the escaping gases is called *thrust*. Thus, if a rocket combustion chamber is equipped with a fixed opening, called a nozzle, through which the expanded gases can escape, the direction of the projectile on which the rocket engine is mounted can be determined. That is why the nozzles of a rocket engine are aligned along a line drawn through the center of the missile.

News of the Chinese success with simple rcokets spread to Europe where, in the 1200's, work in this area was already in progress by an English monk and scientist, Roger Bacon. The Italians were also interested in rocketry, history recording that they used rockets in battles in the thirteenth century.

About this time there began a search for other ways to use this newly found source of power. Soon it was discovered that a stone or piece of metal could be thrown, or thrust, a great distance at enormous speed when driven out of a tube by the explosive rocket mixture. This, of course, was the beginning of today's gun. Understandably, the early guns were crude and not very accurate.

Pirates on the high seas during the 1400's found rockets useful when raiding merchant ships. Still the problem with both early rockets and early guns was that they were extremely inaccurate and otherwise hard to control. Only slight changes in the powder mixture would produce different burning rates, thus changing the amount of thrust produced.

To England's William Congreve, the rocket had great possibilities. During the early 1800's he conducted many rocket experiments, some with startling success. Congreve had an advantage over other rocket pioneers in that he understood much better the basic principles of rocket operation and the forces that acted on a rocket in flight. Also, he knew well the principles of thrust put forth by Newton, and spent considerable time investigating ways of improving the efficiency of rockets. Congreve soon discovered that he had much greater success with his rockets when he shaped the mixture into a solid cake. He also found it necessary to eliminate loose grains or cracks in the container when he loaded the mixture. But probably the most important of his discoveries was that the amount of propellant surface area being burned was directly proportional to the amount of thrust being produced.

Many of the Congreve principles of solid-propellant rocketry have helped lead to the vast number of different types of solid motors we have today. (Engineers call a solid propulsion system a *motor;* they call a liquid propulsion system an *engine.*) Solid motors vary in size from two inches in diameter, used for propellant settling rockets and retro-rockets, to the giant 260-inch-diameter solid motor that has been tested by scientists of the National Aeronautics and Space Administration (NASA). As might be expected, man now has learned much more about solid rocket motors than Congreve could have ever dreamed. He can control the thrust in any manner he pleases.

There are basically two types of solid-propellant grain configurations. The first of these is called *restricted burning;* that is, the propellant burns only on the end face like a cigarette. Since this is the minimum area that could be burning, the thrust produced is quite low but the burning time is quite long. Some of the uses for this type of rocket motor are for jet-assisted takeoff (JATO) units, artillery rockets and guided missile sustainer sections.

The other form of solid-propellant rocket motors is called *unrestricted burning.* In this rocket the grain is allowed to burn on more than just the rear end. To accomplish this action, some of the propellant is removed from the center of' the motor along its entire length. There are many different shapes or patterns that can be removed, the design depending on the thrust required for the missile. One of the most widely used grain patterns is the star shape. You can easily understand that as the burning continues along the entire length of the motor, the surface area, with a pattern removed, increases as does the thrust. You can visualize this better by thinking of the unrestricted type as burning from inside to outside, while the restricted type burns from the back of the motor to the front. With its high thrust and short burn time, the unrestricted type of rocket is used in first-stage boosters in order to drive missiles quickly to a high velocity.

Getting back to Congreve's early rocket efforts, we find that his war-torn homeland benefited greatly from his rockets. Having mounted the rockets on ships, the British were able to reverse the tide of some imminent defeats and inflict great damage on the armies of Napoleon. But the Congreve rockets probably had their most effective use during the War of 1812 between the United States and Great Britain. The British siege of Fort McHenry with rocket barges prompted a young American sailor, Francis Scott Key, to scribble down the now-famous phrase, "the rockets' red glare."

Following the War of 1812, there were, surprisingly, long periods of time when the military use of rocketry was almost nonexistent. The unsolved problem once again was as it had always been—failure to control the rocket power accurately.

All the early rocket pioneers accomplished their limited goals by using solid propellants, very little, if any, work being done with liquid propellants until the nineteenth century.

Much of the rocket progress in the nineteenth century and early in the twentieth century came from the engineering genius of three men—a Russian, Konstantin Ziolkovsky; Austrian-born Herman Oberth and an American, Dr. Robert Goddard.

Although handicapped with poor hearing and lacking a formal education, Ziolkovsky might have been a more famous person had he not been of a shy, retiring nature. A schoolmaster, he was much more interested in performing research than in receiving recognition from his scientific writings. The fact that his reports were quite complicated and written only in Russian also helped to keep his knowledge of rocketry almost unknown for a time.

Ziolkovsky, probably the first to use a wind tunnel, decided that the solid-fuel rocket would not be practical for space travel. His investigations showed that a liquid fuel would operate much better, and time has proved him correct. The fuel Ziolkovsky selected was probably quite similar to the propellant used by the giant first-stage F-1 engines on the Saturn V.

It was not until 1924 that the importance of Ziolkovsky's writings was realized, and at about that time many of his reports were finally published. At his death in 1935, he was considered as one of the great heroes of the Soviet Union. How much sooner the Soviets could have achieved their famous space successes had Ziolkovsky's work been recognized earlier will never be known. But there is no doubt that Ziolkovsky laid much of the groundwork from which the Soviet space achievements have come.

What Ziolkovsky was to the Soviet Union, Herman Oberth was to the Germans. Oberth, like Ziolkovsky, realized early the promise of rocket power and wrote of imaginary trips into space. Many of his themes on rocketry proved too complicated for the common man, but by this time interest in rocketry had advanced so much that his writings sold well regardless.

Oberth, experimenting with liquid oxygen in small motors, provided a scientific breakthrough when he found exhaust velocities to be quite high. But Oberth experienced many problems in the handling of liquid oxygen. Its temperature is so low that it almost instantly freezes any moisture that comes anywhere near it. Even today with our scientific techniques, the use of liquid oxygen presents many handling problems. This "supercold" liquid, called a cryogenic, has been used from the time of Oberth to today's powerful Saturn rockets.

The Saturn V uses liquid oxygen as an oxidizer in all three of its stages. Lox can be utilized effectively with kerosene-type fuels, such as the commonly used American rocket fuel, RP-1, or with other cryogenics, such as liquid hydrogen. Lox evaporates or "boils off"; therefore, the boiled-off lox must be continuously replenished between the completion of fueling operations and launch. This technique is known as "topping off."

The third, and undoubtedly the best known of the three early rocketeers, was Dr. Robert H. Goddard of Clark University, Worcester, Massachusetts, whose achievements were so many and varied that he has become known as the "Father of American Rocketry." Not only did he develop a workable liquid-fueled rocket engine, but he also designed and successfully launched a rocket using it. Dr. Goddard also attacked and solved one of the major problems plaguing rockets through the ages—stabilizing the rocket during its flight. He accomplished this stabilization by using the gyroscope.

Gyroscopes have long been used on ships for stability on the high seas, to make it possible for the ship to have a smooth ride even though the waves are high. The gyroscope principle in a rocket works in exactly the same way. A gyroscope consists of a cylinder which spins at a high speed on a fixed rod. The centrifugal force generated by the rapidly spinning cylinder resists any movement of the spin axis. Of course, the larger the gyroscope the more powerful this resistance becomes. The gyroscope is one of the major parts of the modern inertial guidance systems used by many of our operational missile systems.

The most visible of Goddard's ideas, however, came from his original thinking on the principle of a multistage rocket. The theory behind this multistage idea was really quite simple, with a number of rockets of decreasing size mounted on top of each other. The lowermost rocket, or the first stage, as it is now called, is the first to be fired, carrying the smaller stages and the useful payload. Once the first stage's fuel supply has been depleted, the burned-out stage is dropped off. This procedure is called jettisoning. The upper stages are then fired in sequence, pushing the payload to still higher velocity. The advantages obtained from the multistage technique are quite easy to see. The first or rearmost stage imparts all of its velocity to the next higher up stage and, by dropping back to earth when it has burned out, decreases the total weight of the vehicle in proportion to its remaining fuel. Goddard predicted that a multistage rocket would be able to reach a speed of about 36,000 feet per second—the speed necessary for the rocket to escape the pull of the earth's gravitational field and be influenced by that of the moon.

Of course, this speed has already been achieved with the Ranger and Surveyor probes. This is also the velocity that will have to be attained by the Saturn V when it drives the Apollo spacecraft toward its moon destination. Imagine how shocked Goddard would be were he alive—he died in 1945—to see a rocket capable of driving about fifty tons to this lunar escape velocity.

While the accomplishments of each of these three rocket pioneers were immense, Goddard was the first actually to translate his complicated theories into workable rockets and patentable devices. He, more than any other person, is responsible for many of the engineering principles behind the large space rockets of today. Unfortunately, however, many of the Goddard discoveries went almost unnoticed during the 1920's and 1930's. This unconcern was due primarily to the Great Depression in the United States. Goddard, handicapped by the lack of sufficient funds, continued to carry on his rocket experiments—but at a very low level.

An ocean away from Goddard, in Germany, much emphasis was being placed on rocket research. Still reeling from defeat in World War I, the Germans were forced to operate under the Treaty of Versailles, which prevented Germany from rearming. The treaty specifically barred the Germans from producing any long-range artillery, all types of cannon and machine guns. But a significant omission in the list was that of rockets, an oversight that did not go unnoticed by the Germans. Named to study the military possibilities of the rocket was a capable young military officer named Walter Dornberger.

Dornberger immediately found out that neither German research organizations nor German industries had the knowledge to provide him assistance in his rocket undertaking. This situation led him to build his own small rocket experimental station south of Berlin. Among his employees was a young engineer, Werner Von Braun, who was named a technical assistant.

Von Braun, whose parents had hoped their son would follow his father's footsteps in agriculture, had been fascinated by the stars since he was small. Von Braun joined the German Society for Space Travel, and participated in building and testing small rockets. Dornberger was deeply impressed with the brilliance of Von Braun, but he sometimes had difficulty in persuading his assistant to pursue practical rocketry research rather than to dream of space travel. Today, Dr. Von Braun is director of NASA's sprawling Marshall Space Flight Center at Redstone Arsenal, Alabama. This agency is responsible for the development of space launch vehicles.

In 1932 the first actual rocket engine was tested, with what turned out to be disastrous results. An explosion destroyed a large part of the test facilities. However, in spite of the explosion, lack of materials and other handicaps, the Germans had several minor successes.

Dornberger, now armed with his breakthroughs, meager as they were, and assured of the potential of the rocket, pushed the government hard to acquire new facilities for a massive rocket research effort. The government listened, and the Peenemunde Project was born. Germany, it turned out, would spend forty million dollars on this project up until the time it was captured by the Allies at the end of World War II.

As Germany was, in 1937, starting to flex its military muscle, its main interest was in developing weapons of vast power. Work, then, was soon started on a new rocket program called the A-4, which was later to be known to the world as the infamous V-2 (Vengeance Weapon Number 2). After many technical setbacks, including redesign, the first V-2, in a successful launch, traveled 125 miles. A total of 4300 V-2 rockets were fired during the war, with about 1100 of them landing in England.

The V-2, the world's first ballistic missile, was a supersonic (faster than the speed of sound) rocket which was launched from the vertical position. Its preprogramed guidance system automatically pitched it over toward the target shortly after launching. The maximum flight range was about 200 miles, during which it attained a top speed of about 3300 miles per hour. The V-2's measured forty-seven feet in length and five and one-half feet in diameter. Its total launch weight was more than fourteen tons, including a warhead weighing nearly a ton. The great effectiveness of the V-2 lay in its unlikelihood of being intercepted. Once the preprogramed turn had been made, the V-2 effectively became an artillery projectile which bore down on the target at blinding speed.

As the German military situation worsened near the end of the war, the battle lines were pushed so far back into Germany that all of the important Allied targets were beyond the 200-mile range of the V-2. Once this happened, the effectiveness of the V-2 was ended, thus finishing the Germans' rocket role in World War II.

One can hardly keep from wondering what would have happened in World War II if the V-2 had emerged several years earlier. The war could have had quite a different outcome. At the least, wider use of the V-2 might have made an Allied victory much more difficult. Not since the days of Peenemunde has the rocket been without respect, and it probably never will be.

3

The United States
Learns

In 1945, peace came to the world and, along with the cessation of the fighting, the dissassembly of the victorious United States war machine. To the Germans, peace meant the end of their rocket era. Momentarily shattered were the dreams of the German rocketeers, whose work, although it did not win the war for Germany, had been amazingly successful in the eyes of many persons. But as the war ground to a close, these rocket engineers did not go unnoticed. The United States and Russia considered these men prizes of great scientific value and struggled frantically to capture them. In the past, victorious nations have nearly always exacted territory and other property from their defeated enemies, but this is probably the first time that the spoils of war included some of the loser's scientists. The effort of the victorious nations to capture the scientists was evidence enough of the high scientific caliber of the men involved. The United States fared quite well in acquiring Von Braun and a large number of other German engineers in an operation known as "Project Paperclip."

Along with the acquisition of nearly all of the rocket scientists, the United States was also fortunate in being able to confiscate more than three hundred boxcar loads of V-2 parts from an underground manufacturing plant. Approximately one hundred V-2 rockets were later assembled from these parts. It was generally believed at the time that the V-2 would prove to be the beginning for any future rocket successes that the United States could expect.

The United States military was eager to use both the ideas of these German rocketeers and their V-2 equipment, which had been shipped to the United States. But, once again, as had been true so many times in the history of rocketry, public support was lacking. After all, many said, the war was over! People were tired of hearing about guns and rockets. Public sentiment was definitely against any further rocket development following World War II.

Nevertheless, at the war's end the United States Army, the Navy and several university research groups gathered in an unlikely, almost totally uninhabited location in the southwestern United States to test the V-2 war materials. This spot, to be known as the White Sands Proving Grounds (WSPG), in southern New Mexico, encompasses four thousand square miles. Tucked between two mountain ranges, this test center, in the begnning at least, was almost as quiet and isolated as the moon surface must be. With commercial and private aircraft flights excluded from the area, White Sands was the place chosen for the German scientists, bringing their now silent weapons of war, to continue their dreams for space travel. The original party at White Sands consisted of only 160 men, whose task it was to build the meager facilities with which to test the V-2 rockets. The first mission of the rocket technicians was to learn all they could about the German rocket equipment. Many V-2's were fired to accomplish this end.

Today the White Sands Missile Range, as it is now known, has become one of the largest rocket test ranges in the country. The range is now basically involved with the testing of short-range rockets, antitank guided missiles and surface-to-air antiaircraft missiles. The long-range missiles and huge space launch vehicles, having long since outgrown White Sands, are now launched from the Air Force Western Test Range at Vandenberg Air Force Base in California and from the sprawling NASA spaceport at Cape Kennedy, Florida.

The first major purely American rocket program to be carved out at White Sands was known as the "WAC-Corporal," named after the military rank. A small sounding rocket preceding the corporal had been called the "Private." The name "Corporal" was later given to a 75-mile-range surface-to-surface missile of the United States Army. The Corporal was later replaced by a single-stage solid-propellant missile known as the "Sergeant."

The WAC-Corporal, about sixteen feet long, was liquid-fueled with aniline and red fuming nitric acid. The Corporal was boosted during its first few seconds of flight by a solid propellant. The WAC-Corporal was what is called a "vertical probe," a sounding rocket sent aloft to investigate the mysteries of the earth's upper atmosphere. On October 11, 1945, the WAC set an altitude record of 235,000 feet—almost 45 miles. Much information about the density and temperature of the upper atmosphere was radioed back to the ground. A somewhat larger atmospheric rocket, the "Aerobee," was also developed at White Sands during this time.

By 1946 the German V-2 rockets, readily convertible from weapons of war to their new peacetime use of upper atmosphere data gathering, had replaced the WAC-Corporal. Serving as "flying test-beds" for new rocket engine developments, the V-2's easily broke the altitude record of the WAC-

Corporal by traveling 114 miles into the uncharted reaches of the upper atmosphere.

It was about this time that the multistage rocket principle, proposed many years before by Dr. Goddard, was attempted in a program called "Project Bumper." The plan involved using the V-2 as a first stage topped by the WAC-Corporal, which served as the second stage. This two-stage combination, it was believed, would be able to use the propulsive energy of both rocket vehicles in a single launch.

Hope was indeed high among the technicians who toiled over the sixth Project Bumper vehicle on February 24, 1949. Standing 60 feet high, the vehicle looked quite strange poised against the quiet desolation of the sage-covered New Mexico desert. When the countdown had reached zero, the V-2's rocket engine suddenly came to life, spewing out the orange flame and white smoke characteristic of its alcohol and liquid oxygen propulsion system. Then, hesitating on its concrete launch pad for what seemed an agonizingly long time, the propulsion system finally built up its maximum thrust, and the vehicle slowly rose into the beautiful desert sky. With the WAC-Corporal nestled in its nose, the V-2 burned out at an altitude of 70 miles, at a speed greater than 3000 miles per hour. This speed was added to the WAC-Corporal, which then burst into life and quickly streaked away from its burned-out V-2 first stage. The momentum of the V-2's velocity continued to carry the burned-out V-2 stage upward until gravity pulled it back to earth.

The WAC-Corporal second stage had burned for about 40 seconds, shooting up another 180 miles, before starting the long trip back to earth. It is interesting to note that when the WAC-Corporal's engine had shut down, the rocket was still below 100 miles in altitude—far short of the 250-mile altitude it later reached. How could this be possible? This happened because of the 5150-mile-per-hour velocity attained by the complete vehicle and the low atmospheric drag on the vehicle. The atmosphere is almost nonexistent at altitudes of more than 100 miles. The WAC-Corporal actually had coasted upward the last 150 miles, being slowed only by the earth's gravity.

So successful were the flights of the Bumper vehicles that a Naval Research Laboratory rocket program, known as the Viking, was halted. But the Viking cancellation was to be only temporary, for it was soon realized that the V-2's were in alarmingly short supply, and, of course, no more were being produced.

The Viking was a single-stage, pencil-thin rocket just over 41 feet long. Resembling a silver dart, the Viking, like the V-2, used alcohol and liquid oxygen for its propellant. Many of Dr. Goddard's principles, as well as the V-2 devices, found their way into the Viking design. A huge undertaking for the United States, which had no experience in building a vehicle of this size, the Viking nevertheless became a very successful system. Among the many achievements of the Viking rockets was a launch from the deck of a ship to an altitude of 106 miles. Viking rockets were used until 1951, when they were applied as test vehicles for Project Vanguard—America's first artificial earth satellite program. So, in a small and important way, the research data supplied by the early Viking missiles contributed to the meager United States knowledge of space phenomena at the time. This information also provided sound footing for advancement to more ambitious programs which will soon lead us to the moon and stars.

The Viking's flight was similar to that of many other vertical rockets in that most of its altitude was obtained by coasting straight up after the main engine had shut off. The maximum altitude attained by the Viking was 158 miles, yet the engine burned out at an altitude of only 30 miles after achieving a speed of 4300 miles per hour.

Many other new rocket ideas were carried out at the White Sands Proving Grounds during the late 1940's and the early 1950's. One of the most interesting was the development of the "balloon launch technique." In this method, a small sounding rocket was attached to a lighter-than-air gas-filled balloon. The balloon then towed the rocket up to an altitude of many thousands of feet, where the rocket was ignited and in many cases blasted up through the balloon. The "free-ride" provided by the balloon added thousands of feet to the rocket's altitude, as it didn't have to fight through the air resistance, or "drag," produced by the dense portions of the earth's lower atmosphere. A most ingenious idea, indeed!

Although probably the greatest interest in these early American rocket activities lay in investigation of the upper atmosphere, many other rocket-oriented programs also were begun about this time. These were the initial developments for the rocket-powered surface-to-air missiles (SAM's). This type of military missile is used to intercept and destroy manned aircraft whose speed made them almost impossible targets for existing antiaircraft guns. Among the programs initiated during this time were the Nike Ajax and the Bomarc. Many other SAM missiles, such as the Navy's three T's—Terrior, Talos and Tartar—are also being researched, along with many aircraft mounted air-to-air (AAM's) and air-to-surface missiles (ASM's).

The next American missile effort was the Redstone Missile Program. Designed to support the Army, this missile had a range of 300 miles. The program, initiated in the fall of 1950, was given highest priority. The orginal German technicians and White Sands engineers were basically in charge of the program, which was carried out at the Redstone Arsenal in Huntsville, Alabama. Redstone became the name of the rocket—after the red-colored, clayish soil of that northern Alabama location.

The Redstone in the beginning was a single-stage missile incorporating many of the successful features of the old V-2 system. The propulsion system used liquid oxygen as the oxidizer and an alcohol mixture as the fuel. Through modifications and improvements, the Redstone's rocket engine was finally rated at 75,000 pounds of thrust.

The Redstone was the first ballistic missile to utilize an all-inertial guidance system. Using this system, the Redstone was able to fly a preplanned trajectory and to correct itself in flight. The control of the missile was accomplished by carbon vanes which protruded into the engine's exhaust and directed the exhaust gas flow. As the Redstone was the first large ballistic missile to be employed in the field by United States troops, it was by necessity a mobile system. This means that it had to be capable of being moved to a new location within a short period of time, so that the firing battery could not be pinpointed by the enemy. The Redstone was placed in the North Atlantic Treaty Organization (NATO) defense in 1958, but was replaced by the solid-propellant Pershing system in the mid-1960's.

The Redstone proved its worth—not only as a ballistic missile, but also as the lower stage for a high-altitude research

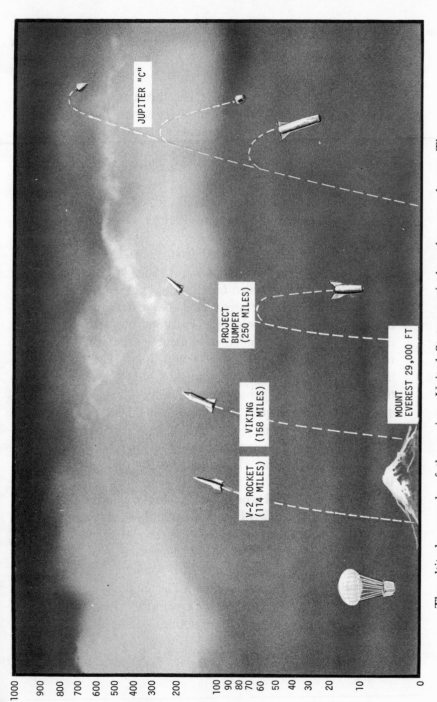

The altitude records of the various United States vertical probes are shown. The highest altitude was achieved by the Jupiter C system.

rocket known as the Jupiter C. The thrust in the Jupiter C, propelled by the Redstone system using a new fuel, had been increased by more than 8000 pounds, thus enabling the Jupiter C to break the existing altitude record held by the WAC-Corporal. The Jupiter C had two additional high-speed solid-propellant upper stages on top of its modified Redstone booster. These upper stages rested in a cone-shaped tube which was spun electrically just before launch to provide stability to the missile in flight.

The first Jupiter C was fired from Cape Canaveral (now Cape Kennedy) on September 20, 1956. Carrying no guidance system and controlled only by the angle at which it was aimed, the Redstone booster lofted the vehicle to an altitude of 200 miles. At this point, the Redstone was jettisoned and the upper two stages ignited in sequence, driving the payload to the amazing altitude of nearly 700 miles. The third stage hit the earth 3000 miles downrange. Jupiter C was also used to test early ballistic missile reentry vehicles which, mounted atop the booster, experienced the searing heat produced by the atmosphere as they plummeted to earth. The reentry vehicles which were tested were to become parts of a new long-range ballistic missile known as the Jupiter Intermediate-Range Ballistic Missile.

The Jupiter IRBM would be the next of a large family of missiles to be developed by the German-headed team at Redstone Arsenal. About three feet larger in diameter than its little brother, the Redstone, the Jupiter used a single liquid-propellant engine generating 150,000 pounds of thrust—more than twice that of the Redstone. The engine was mounted on hinges, an arrangement which permitted it to pivot and, therefore, make any needed corrections during the flight. Although the 1500-mile-range Jupiter was basically designed as a weapon of war, scientists and engineers immediately realized its potential for use in space. Later the Jupiter was to add materially to our knowledge of space by performing a number of successful space launches.

As impressive as the Redstone and Jupiter were, there was a certain reluctance on the part of the military planners to adopt this type of weapon completely to the exclusion of all other types. All systems, it was agreed, must be tested. Therefore another family of rockets, the air-breathers, appeared in the late 1940's. These systems utilized solid-propellant boosters which drove the missiles during the first part of the flight. Following booster shutdown, the missile's flight was continued by means of either an air-breathing turbojet or a ramjet. The specific systems which evolved were the long-range surface-to-air Bomarc, the thousand-mile-range Matador and the ship-mounted Regulus.

Another such system, the Navaho, canceled even after $700,000,000 had been spent on it, used two large strap-on boosters and two ramjet sustainer motors. One of the more impressive and successful air-breathing missiles of the late 1940's, although it experienced many mechanical difficulties in early testing, was the Snark—America's first intercontinental ballistic missile (ICBM). "Snark-Infested Waters," said a sign, put there by a joker, following a number of early unsuccessful Snark launches at Cape Canaveral (Kennedy). The Snark, as was true with many of the other air-breathing missiles of this type, closely resembled an airplane, having both wings and a tail.

Most of these rocket developments, from the V-2's up through the Redstone and the Jupiter, were made by or under the direction of the Army. However, interest in ballistic missiles was beginning to bud in the other two branches of the armed services—the Navy and the Air Force.

Wishing to convert the Jupiter for use on submarines, the Navy took part in the early development work at Redstone Arsenal. But it was soon learned that the maintenance problems involved with a liquid-fueled missile such as the Jupiter would prevent its use aboard a submerged submarine. The Navy then abandoned the Jupiter program and began developing—successfully, it turned out—the solid-fueled IRBM which we know today as the Polaris. Since the time of the first Polaris, there have been two other improved versions, and work is now well advanced on the Poseidon, which promises to surpass the capability of even the most advanced Polaris models. The Polaris, armed with nuclear warheads, is now stationed around the world in nuclear-powered submarines.

At the time the Army was developing the Jupiter, the Air Force began a parallel development on the Thor IRBM. Although these systems used similar propulsion and guidance devices, a great deal of rivalry developed as to which of the two was better. The arguments reached such a heated state that the Secretary of Defense decided to assign certain range responsibilities to each of the two services involved. All ranges up to 200 miles belonged to the Army, he decided, while anything greater than 200 miles was the responsibility of the Air Force. This decision meant that the Army was out of the large ballistic missile business. Actually, neither the Jupiter nor the Thor was ever operated to any degree in United States, although Thor was installed in a number of places in Great Britain by the Royal Air Force.

Working against further development of the IRBM was the feeling of many military men that the best long-range weapon was the airplane. After all, hadn't the B-17 and the B-29 long-range bombers been the deciding factor in the World War II victory? It logically followed, they argued, that improvements to manned aircraft would be the realistic approach. Nevertheless, a large number of Air Force officers pleaded zealously, and finally an American ICBM program was born in the early 1950's. The program, called the Atlas, struggled along on meager funds during its first three years. It was not until reports told of great interest and progress in long-range ballistic missiles in the Soviet Union that the Atlas program started to gain momentum.

The Atlas, a truly amazing weapon for its time, surpassed all of the previous American missile accomplishments. Used in the Atlas were two heretofore untried concepts—a pressurized body section and a stage-and-a-half staging technique.

The pressurized technique was brought about by the need to lighten the vehicle. Previous missiles had used steel skins no heavier than necessary to support structure of the missile and still be strong enough to withstand the tremendous forces during its trajectory. However, since the Atlas would be required to throw a heavy nuclear warhead 5000 miles, the need for lightening the missile became obvious. This was accomplished by using the pressure of the propellants pushing against the sides of the missile. Pressurized anyway to aid their flow to the engines, the propellants thus added rigidity to the structure of the missile and allowed the use of a much thinner and lighter metal skin.

The stage-and-a-half idea was brought about by the difficulties encountered in starting a rocket at high altitudes. Propellants at high altitudes, acting under the reduced force of the earth's gravity, have a tendency to float around in the tank, thus making it very difficult to start the engines properly. It was decided, therefore, that the Atlas would start all of its main engines at lift-off—two 135,000-pound thrust boosters and one 100,000-pound sustainer. The booster engines burned a predetermined length of time, and then were jettisoned along with their protective covers. The Atlas, now rid of the weight of the booster propulsion systems, continued its powered flight with the sustainer engine. This technique incorporated the advantages of the multistage concept, which had been suggested by Dr. Goddard, but it did not have the early problems associated with starting a rocket engine at high altitude. Precious weight was saved, too, when both the sustainer and the boosters were fed from the same fuel tanks and when a single bulkhead was made to serve between the fuel and the oxidizer.

As the Atlas was a new and revolutionary concept in many ways, it was decided that a parallel program would be carried out to assure that any weaknesses found in the Atlas design might be corrected by the other program and thus probably make possible the successful operation of the Atlas in a shorter time. This second program, which became known as the Titan ICBM, was different in many ways from the Atlas. It used a conventional type of airframe, a different propulsion system and two distinct powered stages. The Titan also was designed to be launched from an underground silo; the Atlas had been engineered for an above-the-ground launch. Many of the Titan's parts were interchangeable with those of the Atlas. This parallel development technique was first tried with the joint Jupiter-Thor development program. Both the Atlas and the Titan development programs were successful, and both eventually were used in defense operations by the Strategic Air Command of the United States Air Force.

The large size and maintenance problems of these two systems, however, made them less than perfect for their role in national defense. The handling of dangerous liquid propellants underground presented many problems. So it was decided that a solid-propellant ICBM would be better, for the missile could remain fully fueled for long periods and thus be able to react much more quickly in case of war. An outgrowth of this decision was the Boeing-built Minuteman, to which much of the Atlas and Titan experience was added. The Minuteman has been placed around the United States in great numbers.

The United States began its modest rocket program immediately after World War II, and has made encouraging progress since that time. Beginning with captured German V-2 equipment, this country has developed a whole stable of reliable missiles. Amazing progress was made especially in the development of guidance and control systems for placing the newly developed nuclear warheads on their targets.

Although many of the systems we have discussed are now considered quite primitive, they were nevertheless the first tottering footsteps toward the giant Saturn rockets of today. Many of these first systems also served as the first-stage boosters for the early space launches of the United States. Without these stepping-stone rockets, the story of Saturn V, the Moon Rocket, would be far in the future.

4

Early Space

On October 4, 1957, the newspapers of the world splashed the news of the Soviet Union's launching of the world's first artificial satellite. Russia rightfully felt proud of its space engineers, and the world applauded the scientific breakthrough. But from a startled and embarrassed United States public came the question, "How could the United States, undeniably the world's greatest technical and industrial nation, be outdone by a country that suffered such great damage during World War II?" The lesson was clear. Although the United States long had had the capability to accomplish the feat, it had not pursued the work as diligently as had the Soviet Union. Another question that immediately came to the minds of all Americans was, "When is the United States also going to place a satellite in orbit?"

The United States had first become interested in earth satellites during the 1940's, when some research on the idea was done by both the Army and the Navy. The Navy proposed constructing a single-stage launch vehicle using a liquid-hydrogen-fueled propulsion system. The lift-off thrust for the vehicle was to be about 230,000 pounds from the main propulsion system, but the satellite was actually to be placed in a circular orbit by a small secondary solid propulsion system. The proposal was ahead of its time, incorporating many advanced concepts.

However, this idea and another proposed by the Rand Corporation were never to be followed through on. No one in authority was ready to accept the idea that a small satellite could be placed in orbit around the earth. Even if the United States could do so, it was asked, would the heavy cost be justified; what would a successful launching prove? And so it was to be ten long years from the time of these early proposals before an official United States earth satellite program was inaugurated.

During the early 1950's the United States' ideas for orbiting a satellite changed from the single-stage concept to the use of a ballistic missile as a first-stage booster topped by small multiple upper stages. The successful vertical probe Bumper and Viking programs had provided valuable data about this system in their high-altitude launches.

The energy required to place a satellite into a low earth orbit is only slightly more than that of a vertical probe or ballistic missile. In a vertical probe the vehicle flies a near-vertical trajectory, and the payload coasts until it is stopped at its apogee, or highest point, by the earth's gravity. In the flight of a ballistic missile, the vehicle is tilted over shortly after lift-off and burns out nearly parallel to the earth's surface. The momentum obtained by the missile will tend to push it far downrange instead of upward, as with the vertical probe.

In order to place a satellite into a low earth orbit, it is necessary for the vehicle to obtain a velocity of about 17,500 miles per hour. This orbital velocity will enable a satellite to circle the earth completely in about ninety minutes. Orbital velocity is the speed required for the satellite's outward pressure, called centrifugal force, to counteract the earth's gravity, which, of course, exerts an inward pull on the satellite. The closer the satellite's orbit is to the earth, the higher the orbital velocity must be for the vehicle to remain in orbit. Not to be overlooked, too, is the fact that the rocket stage directly below the satellite, commonly called the orbit injection stage, will also go into orbit. More often than not, satellites are placed into elliptical or egg-shaped orbits, with the high portion called the apogee and the low portion called the perigee. Elliptical orbits occur when there is an excess velocity at the orbit injection point for a circular orbit of that particular altitude. The velocities of a satellite in an elliptical orbit vary, with the highest speeds occurring at the perigee.

Because of the earth's atmosphere, a vehicle that has obtained orbital velocity cannot remain in orbit forever. Although the atmosphere is very thin at high altitude, it slowly but surely retards the velocity of orbiting objects, of whatever weight or shape they may be. This atmospheric drag, as it is called, will cause the satellite's orbit to decay and eventually plunge the satellite to a flaming death through the dense layers of atmosphere that surround the earth. Having learned much about this atmospheric drag on the life of orbiting objects, space engineers can quite accurately predict their duration. Of course, vehicles in higher orbits, sometimes called higher energy orbits, will be affected less by the earth's atmosphere and will have significantly longer lives, sometimes as long as hundreds of years.

Engineers can plan to bring a vehicle back to earth after some specified time, rather than allowing it to decay in orbit. This can be done in two ways. The vehicle could be slowed by reverse-firing "retro-rockets," which would retard its orbit velocity and bring it to earth. The second method is to orient the vehicle toward the earth and fire a forward thrusting propulsion system, actually driving the vehicle out of orbit.

On July 29, 1955, more than two years before Sputnik I, the following announcement was issued from the White House: "The President has approved plans for going ahead with the launching of small, unmanned, earth-circling satellites as part of the United States' participation in the International Geophysical Year, which takes place between July, 1957, and December, 1958." The announcement also stated that the responsibility for the new satellite program would lie with the Department of Defense, whose first task would be to select the launch vehicle. Since none of the launch vehicles in existence had been designed to do this job, it was decided to modify some existing vertical probe or missile. Three basic proposals were considered.

At first the most attractive possibility, in terms of performance, lay in the Atlas ICBM, then in an early development stage. However, the fact that it was in this early stage ruled out its immediate use. Even though modifying the Atlas for space applications was not possible at that time, the Atlas today is a mainstay of the American space launch vehicle family. Another proposal in the effect to lauch America's first satellite involved using the already existing Jupiter C, which consisted of the reliable Redstone ballistic missile topped by two solid-propellant upper stages. It was eventually decided, however, that the efficiency of this vehicle was too low· to allow it to place in orbit a payload of sufficient size. The proposal finally adopted was a system employing a new, highly efficient launch system, to be called the Vanguard, which had two liquid and one solid propellant stages and relied on a gimbaled, or movable, rocket engine for first stage control.

The Vanguard, without the customary guidance fins on the first stage, resembled a giant bullet. Most previous rockets had used fins to control the missile's direction during the first part of the flight. Since fins were much less effective in the thinner air at higher altitudes, they had never been used anywhere on upper stages. However, the gimbaled motor technique, introduced by the Vanguard, provided a much more effective way of controlling the missile's flight than did fins.

It was decided that the Vanguard would be flight-tested from the newly established facilities at Cape Canaveral. White Sands Proving Ground, where much of the Navy's experience with the Viking and Aerobee rockets had been acquired, was ruled out because burned-out stages might fall into populated areas.

The next two years of work on the Vanguard program moved along successfully at the Cape. Launch and tracking facilities were constructed and tested, and early versions of the Vanguard were successfully fired, carrying large payloads to altitudes greater than 100 miles.

Then, when the Russians placed Sputnik I in orbit in October, 1957, all eyes turned to the United States' only active satellite program—the Vanguard. The United States should place a satellite into orbit now, many Americans said. But the Vanguard was still just an experimental vehicle; it had not even been flown with its three powered stages. The clamor for action had its effect, however, and the Navy decided reluctantly to use the untested Vanguard to try to place a satellite into orbit. But the Vanguard's first-stage engine failed shortly after lift-off, and the rocket fell back on the launch

Launching of the Vanguard from its launch pad at Cape Canaveral (Kennedy), Florida.

pad with a deafening explosion. The United States not only had been beaten into space by the Soviets, but its highly publicized first launch also had been a failure.

One month before the first launch by Vanguard, the Army also had been given a go-ahead to attempt a satellite launch as soon as possible. The launch vehicle selected was the Juno 1, which was basically a Jupiter C with the addition of a fourth solid-propellant stage. Plans called for the Juno 1 to toss a satellite weighing about eighteen pounds into orbit. With the failure of the Vanguard, the prospect of being first in United States space spurred the Redstone Arsenal team to work day and night preparing for their first launch try. On January 31, 1958, only eighty-four days after the project had received the official go-ahead, Juno 1 placed Explorer I into orbit. This first successful launch carried the experimental equipment that detected the Van Allen radiation belts which encircle the earth.

Lifting majestically from its pad at 10:55 P.M. of that not-to-be forgotten day, the Juno 1 quickly gained speed and then pitched over onto its programmed trajectory. The upper stages and payload were separated from the first stage shortly after the first stage had burned out. The first stage was then slowed down and pushed out of the way by small rockets. Following the jettisoning of the protective shroud, the second stage was ignited, and this was followed in rapid succession by the ignition of the third and fourth stages. The orbit altitude for Explorer I had been obtained by the time the second stage had started. In other words, the purpose of the final three upper stages was only to add enough velocity to the satellite to place it in orbit.

Since Juno 1 was quite small, four powered stages were required in order to place the satellite in orbit. Two-stage vehicles are now used for most orbital missions, and more than three stages are seldom used. Of course, the upper stages used today in a two-stage-to-orbit mission are considerably larger than those used on the old Juno 1. In normal operation the second-stage thrust now could be as much as one-fifth to one sixth that of the first-stage booster.

Juno 1 was used six times, successfully placing in orbit three satellites—Explorers I, III and IV. With Explorer IV, the maximum capability of the system was demonstrated with the launching of a twenty-five-pound payload. But when it almost immediately became evident that a greater payload capability was needed, the solution was quite simple—rep ace the Redstone with a larger booster, the Jupiter IRBM. Since the Redstone had successfully performed its function, it logically followed that the larger and more powerful Jupiter should be able to do the job better. And in a short time the payload capabilities of the Juno 2, the name given to the new system, were more than tripled.

The Juno 2 was launched ten times, the final launch occurring in May, 1961. The most exciting achievement of the Juno 2 was the placing of the Pioneer 4 spacecraft into a trajectory which passed quite close to the moon. The Juno 2 used basically the same upper stages as those of the Juno 1 and followed a similar flight profile. Both the Juno 1 and 2 programs made use of existing missile hardware. The upper stages evolved from the Jupiter C, while the first stages in both programs were modified versions of ballistic missiles. This trend of using ballistic missiles as first-stage boosters has continued.

During 1958 the Thor IRBM also made its appearance on the space scene as the booster for the Pioneer satellite. The

Thor, equipped with a number of various upper stages tailored for specific missions, has been one of the most widely used United States space boosters. In mid-1960's the thrust of the Thor first stage was increased by the addition of three solid-propellant rocket motors. Known as the Thrust-Augmented Thor, this variant of the Thor space booster uses the additional solid thrust to increase the Thor payload capability significantly.

Because of its reliability, the Thor system will probably continue to fulfill small weight satellite requirements into the 1970's. Modification of other ballistic missiles for use in space, similar to the changes made in Thor, was further carried out on the largest of our two ballistic missiles, the Atlas and the Titan.

The need for larger payload capability caused changes in the Atlas quite similar to those of the Thor. Equipped with the Able and later the Agena upper stages, the Atlas has launched a large number of USAF and NASA payloads. An early 1960 modification of the Atlas involved the addition of the liquid-hydrogen-fueled Centaur upper stage, which increased its low earth orbital payload capability to about 8000 pounds. Atlas, along with the Redstone, also participated in the United States' first man-in-space program—Project Mercury. The Redstone was the boost vehicle for the four suborbital trajectories, and the Atlas lofted our four manned Mercury capsules into orbit.

The Titan ICBM, also modified for space as the launch vehicle for America's second generation two-man spacecraft, performed flawlessly in twelve shots. Titan's thrust was increased in the 1960's with the addition of two 120-inch solid motors strapped to its side in a vehicle called the Titan IIIC. These strap-ons have actually become the first stage,

REDSTONE FAMILY

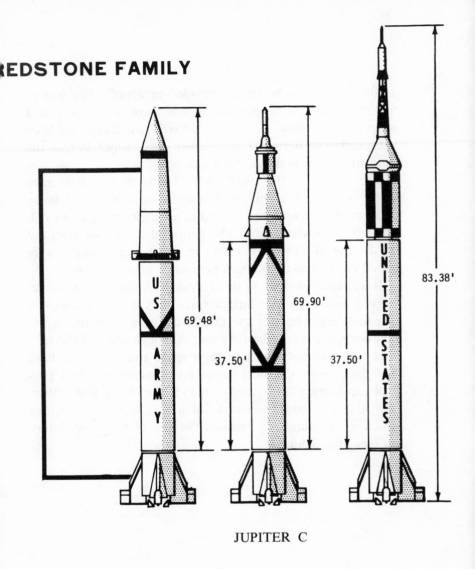

JUPITER C

REDSTONE   MERCURY-REDSTONE

The three versions of the Redstone family shown by this figure are the ballistic missile version on the left, the Jupiter C space launch system, and the Mercury launch vehicle on the right.

as they are the only thrust provided at lift-off. The former first stage has now become the second stage, which is ignited at an altitude when the strap-ons have burned out and been jettisoned. The normal Titan second stage, which is now the third stage, injects the payload into orbit.

The 1950's and the 1960's in the United States would have to be considered by missile historians as a period of many early space accomplishments and as a frantic struggle to catch up with the Soviet Union. The period also was characterized by the use of existing boosters to which upper stages were added in order to accomplish near-earth orbital missions.

It was soon obvious to those closely involved in the rocket work, however, that for further space exploration a completely new and larger booster specifically designed from the beginning for space would be required. Although the ballistic missiles had performed well in their space role, they did have their limitations, the most important of which was their payload capability. Consequently, in 1958 the Army was authorized to begin the development of a new space vehicle, one which would ultimately become the first of the great Saturn rockets—the Saturn I.

5

Saturn I
Comes of Age

After their great success with the Juno 1 and the Juno 2, it was only natural that the Army engineers would continue to design advanced versions of these vehicles. Known as the Juno 3 and the Juno 4 projects, these vehicle programs did not reach the metal-cutting stage, but much was learned from the experience that would in time be used in the Saturn I. The Juno 3 proposal consisted of a multistage rocket using the proven Jupiter as the first stage, with larger solid-propellant upper stages. However, both the Juno 3 and the Juno 4, the latter also a three-stage vehicle, had an orbital payload of only 500 pounds for a 100-mile orbit.

But in order to accomplish an orbital space mission of any importance, it is necessary to place in orbit payloads weighing thousands of pounds instead of hundreds, and this need was considered when the Juno 5 program began. The plan was to develop a new large space booster which, to keep costs down, would use much existing hardware and tooling equipment. Since the desired payload was to be in the 20,000- to 40,000-pound range, a two-stage vehicle would be required, with the first stage having 1,500,000 pounds of thrust. As no existing booster even remotely approached that large thrust figure, the need to develop a new space booster became quite evident. And it was decided that eight of the reliable Jupiter first-stage liquid engines would be used to power this stage.

These engines would be attached to a thrust frame, with four of them mounted together in a fixed position along the center line of the vehicle. The other four would be mounted ninety degrees apart around the outside of the base of the first stage. These outboard engines would be mounted on gimbals, allowing the engines to be controlled during the burn period of the first stage.

Once the problem of the propulsion system had been solved, the matter of tanking the propellants had to be considered. The method finally selected involved the clustering of eight 70-inch-diameter Redstone tanks around a center 105-inch-diameter Jupiter tank. The center tank, as well as four of the outboard Redstone tanks, was completely filled with liquid oxygen. The other four outboard Redstone tanks contained the RP-1 fuel. When the first stage was fully assembled, it was 82 feet long and 21½ feet in diameter, more than twice the size of any previous United States space booster.

The technique used in the Juno 5 first stage is known as a clustered tankage configuration. That is, each engine does not have a separate propellant and oxidizer tank, as was true with the Redstone and the Jupiter. An advantage to the clustered tankage technique is that it is not necessary to run a lox line through the fuel tank, for the fuel and oxidizer are contained separately in clustered tanks with the separate propellants feeding from the bottom. (It is possible, though, to cluster complete propulsion modules, each containing fuel and oxidizer tanks, in order to derive a high thrust booster. This configuration is known as a clustered propulsion module booster.)

Another advantage of Juno 5's clustered tankage configuration was that it possessed an inherent "engine-out" capability.

That is, if one of the engines should prematurely shut down, the fuel that would have been used by this engine would be transferred to the remaining seven engines. If this shutdown does not occur too near the lift-off, it is quite possible that the mission can still be accomplished. This advantage does not exist with the clustered propulsion module concept, since propellants from one module cannot be fed to other engines.

During the early development of the Juno 5, the National Aeronautics and Space Administration (NASA), an organization with responsibility for all civilian space efforts, was established. The Juno 5 and all other Redstone Arsenal space work was absorbed into NASA as the Marshall Space Flight Center at Huntsville, Alabama. Many of the Army space engineers transferred to the new organization, which now, of course, had the responsibility for the development of all space boosters. Juno 5 soon became known as the Saturn C-1 space booster, with the clustered tankage first stage being known as the S-I.

Because of the large diameter of the S-I, the development of an upper stage for it proved troublesome. The Titan missile, with its 120-inch diameter, was seriously considered for a time as the second stage, but finally it was decided that the Titan could not supply the thrust needed.

Consequently, the answer, in 1959, was to develop a new large-diameter second stage to meet the demands. The main reason for the change in plan was the large diameter payload being considered for the Saturn C-1. Use of the ICBM-derived second stage would have greatly restricted the external diameter of the payload. It is possible to place a payload of greater diameter on top of a smaller stage. However, this practice, known as "hammerheading" the payload, presents certain problems, and is not considered good engineering practice. The second stage which was developed for the Saturn C-1 was called the S-IV, and incorporated six 15,000-pound thrust engines. These engines, known as the RL-10 engines and using liquid hydrogen and liquid oxygen as their propellants, provided an overall second-stage thrust of 90,000 pounds. Although these new engines presented many technical problems, it was felt that their increased performance was worth the effort.

The way to measure the efficiency in a propellant combination is to examine its specific impulse (I_{sp}). Specific impulse is a measure of the power or thrust acquired from one pound of propellant consumed in one second. The rate at which the propellant is consumed is identical with the rate at which the exhaust products are expelled, since the propellants are converted directly into exhaust gas. The specific impulse of lox and liquid hydrogen is about 425 seconds, while lox and RP-1 produce an I_{sp} of only about 305 seconds.

Despite the extra performance advantage of the high-energy fuels, liquid hydrogen is not used as a fuel for all boosters because of its low density. In other words, it would take a much larger container to tank an equivalent weight of liquid hydrogen than it would for the same weight of RP-1.

Originally, the Saturn C-1 was to have been a three-stage vehicle topped with a so-called S-V third stage powered by two RL-10 engines. But it was decided in 1961 to eliminate the third stage and reduce the Saturn C-1 to a two-stage vehicle.

The Saturn C-1 flight-test program was initiated from Cape Canaveral (Kennedy) on October 27, 1961. The suborbital mission, to test the operation of the S-I booster, used a de-

he fifth Saturn I launch vehicle, SA-5 mission, is launched from LC 37, Cape ennedy, Florida. The vehicle placed a payload of 37,700 pounds into orbit.

rated S-I first stage having only 1,300,000 pounds of thrust and two dummy upper stages. The mission, which was the first of three Block I vehicles to be so launched in a program known as Project Highwater, was a great success. The last two Block I flight tests, conducted in 1962, were highly dramatic as well as successful, in that 30,000 gallons of water were released in the upper atmosphere.

Employing live second stages, the Block II vehicles used the fully rated booster engines to bring the thrust of the S-I stage up to its design value of 1,500,000 pounds. The purpose of the first three Block II flights was to place portions of the Apollo lunar payload into earth orbit. This provided the first introduction to the environment of space for part of the Apollo payload. The final three Block II vehicles, launched in 1965, each succeeded in placing a Pegasus meteoroid detection satellite into orbit.

Ten tries and ten successes. That was the amazing record of the Saturn C-1, whose name had been changed to Saturn I near the end of the program.

The year 1962 proved to be a time of decision for the Saturn program, as many decisions were made which would affect the shape of the next Saturn launch vehicles. The method of going to the moon was decided upon, one that would use a single large launch vehicle. In order to quicken the program's pace, parts of this new launch vehicle and the lunar payload would be verified in an advanced version of the Saturn I launch vehicle.

The Saturn IB, as this new version was to be known, incorporated many improvements over the Saturn I. Although the first stages of the two rockets were quite similar in size and shape, the Saturn IB's first stage featured a 20,000-pound reduction in weight from that of the Saturn I. This reduction in weight increased the orbital payload and improved the structure factor of the stage. That is, the relationship between the empty stage weight and the loaded stage weight had been decreased. Actually, the closer this relationship can be made to approach zero the more efficiently will that stage perform. Common structure factors are in the range of from .08 to .12. This is to say that the structure weighs from about 8 to 12 percent of the total loaded stage weight.

The S-IB first stage was also uprated 100,000 pounds to 1,600,000 pounds of lift-off thrust. This improvement was accomplished by uprating each of the eight H-1 engines from 188,000 pounds to 200,000 pounds. Other improvements, some of them minor, were made on the S-IB stage as a result of the experience gained from the ten Saturn I launches.

The main differences between the Saturn I and the Saturn IB, however, are to be found in the second stage. The Saturn I utilized the 18-foot-diameter S-IV second stage, which generated 90,000 pounds of thrust. This stage was replaced in the Saturn IB by the Saturn S-IVB stage, which would also find later use as the third stage of the Saturn V lunar launch vehicle. The S-IVB stage, a full 40 inches larger in diameter than the S-IV stage, has a single large engine in comparison to the six small engines of the S-IV. Called the J-2, this new S-IVB engine generated 200,000 pounds of thrust and took advantage of the highly efficient lox–liquid hydrogen propellant combination.

The Saturn IB flight test program, started on February 26, 1966, began with a suborbital ballistic trajectory launch—as had most other similar space programs. Further flights of the Saturn IB will prove the structure and operation of the Apollo spacecraft. The actual orbiting of the three-man Apollo space-craft with men aboard took place in 1968.

With its large orbital payload capability of approximately 40,000 pounds, the Saturn IB also is a prime candidate for performing a number of space missions other than that of placing heavy payloads into low earth orbits. So if the IB were to be fitted with a high-performance third stage, it undoubtedly would be capable of sending approximately 10,000 pounds into an earth escape trajectory or extremely high earth orbits. The liquid-hydrogen-fueled Atlas Centaur upper stage has been considered as a likely candidate for the Saturn IB third stage to accomplish the earth escape trajectory, but no definite program in this direction has as yet been started.

The Saturn IB also lends itself quite nicely to first-stage up-rating, a characteristic that greatly increases its low orbit payload capability. Through experience, it has been determined that the most efficient methods of acquiring payload gains can be obtained by increasing the thrust at lift-off. Although there are several ways to do this, one of the most effective is to introduce certain chemical additives into the oxidizer. A good example of this is the adding of fluorine to the lox oxidizer, which increases both the thrust and the specific impulse of the first stage. And, as a result, the S-IB payload can reach nearly 50,000 pounds. Higher concentrations of fluorine make possible even larger payloads, but definite drawbacks limit the use of this chemical additive. Fluorine is a highly explosive substance, and produces a poisonous gas when burned. It is especially harmful when inhaled by persons.

The best way to improve the orbital performance of the Saturn IB, however, is a method known as "the strap-on technique." The plan involves increasing the lift-off thrust by the

SATURN I CONFIGURATIONS

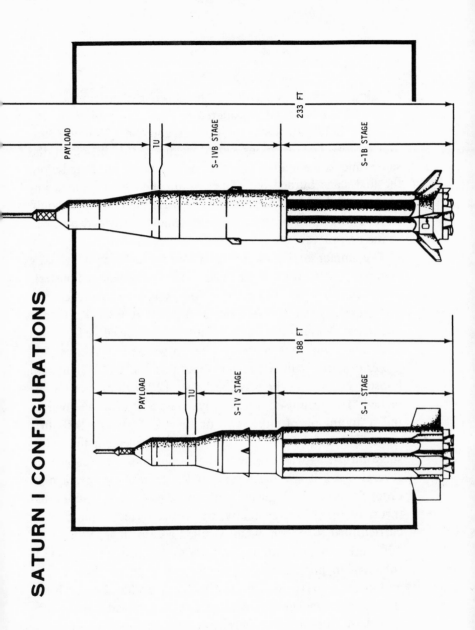

233 FT

PAYLOAD | IU | S-IVB STAGE | S-1B STAGE

188 FT

PAYLOAD | IU | S-1V STAGE | S-1 STAGE

The Saturn I launch vehicle shown on the left uses the 90,000-pound-thrust S-IV second stage. The Saturn IB, on the right, uses the 200,000-pound-thrust S-IVB second stage.

addition to the first stage of "strapped-on" rocket motors. Two motors that have been considered for this application are the ICBM Minuteman first-stage booster and the 120-inch solid-fuel motor. The strap-ons would be lighted at lift-off at the same time as the main stage, and burn to depletion long before the first stage burned out. They would then be jettisoned immediately, since carrying them along with the first stage would offset a large part of the extra performance provided by them in the first place.

The immense size of the S-IB stage can be visualized by comparing it to that of the strapped-on Minuteman boosters. It is hard to believe that those four small items are each a first-stage booster for America's first-line ICBM. Two, four and eight Minuteman motors have been considered in this application, but four motors appear to be the best number.

Performance much greater than that of the Minuteman booster stems from the way the larger 120-inch motors are attached. They are used in two ways. The first of these involves the strapping-on of either two or four 120's to the S-IB first stage. This solid thrust is then used to supplement the main-stage thrust, as was true with the Minuteman application. In several cases it was necessary to lengthen the first stage in order to offset the high pressures produced by the additional thrust of the 120's. Secondly, the strap-on technique can be carried further to form what is called a zero stage. When four 120's are strapped around the S-IB stage, their thrust alone is sufficient to lift the entire launch vehicle off the launch pad and on through the first part of its flight profile. Research has shown that, on certain missions, more payload can be obtained by this method. This zero stage technique would, of

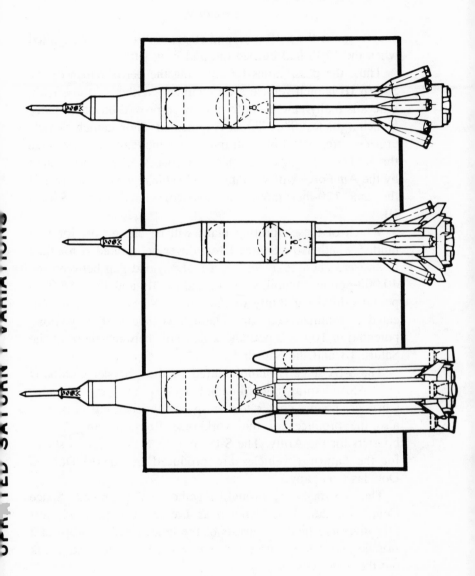

This figure shows three methods that have been considered for upgrading the performance of the Saturn IB launch vehicle. The vehicle on the left incorporates 120-inch solid strap-ons, while the other two vehicles use four and eight Minuteman strap-ons.

course, make the S-IB a second stage, and it would be ignited when the 120's had burned out and been jettisoned.

Thus, the possibilities for uprating the performance of the Saturn IB launch vehicle are unlimited. Neither of these techniques is really new, as both have been proved on other space launch vehicles. The Thrust-Augmented Thor launch vehicle utilizes three solid-fuel strap-ons to increase its first-stage thrust. The zero-stage plan has been successfully demonstrated by the Air Force with its Titan IIIC vehicle, which uses two of the same 120-inch motors as those considered for the Saturn IB.

Which of these uprating plans will be chosen or, for that matter, whether the Saturn IB will ever be uprated is for time to answer. There is, however, a real payload gap between the 40,000-pound capability of the Saturn IB and the 255,000-pound orbital capability of the Saturn V. Studies have indicated a definite need for a launch vehicle with a payload potential of 100,000 pounds, which falls between those of the Saturn IB and the Saturn V.

The S-IB stage is manufactured by the Chrysler Company at NASA's sprawling Michoud facility in New Orleans. Chrysler, no newcomer to the space launcher business, was also the producer of the workhorse Redstone and Jupiter boosters for the Army. The S-IV and the S-IVB second stages for the Saturn I vehicles are produced by the McDonnell Douglas Company.

The two stages are brought together at the Kennedy Space Center for launching. Known as Launch Complex 34, this forty-five-acre facility consists of the launch pad, a propellant storage and a large service structure used to erect and check out the huge rockets.

Enormous as it is, the Saturn I launch vehicle family requires the cooperation of hundreds of private companies working hand in hand with the National Aeronautics and Space Administration. Although the vehicles of the Saturn I family are cold and lifeless as they rest poised on the launch pad, unseen people have played the most important role in its creation. Engineers, scientists, welders and a multitude of other specialists across the country are united by a common bond—Saturn. Every one of them is important because, on a project of this size and complexity, everyone depends on everyone else.

Many of the people of this large team that was formed to build and launch the highly successful Saturns are also a part of a new team with an even greater goal—the sending of three American astronauts to the moon. The project—Apollo. The launch vehicle—Saturn V.

6

The Saturn V
Is Born

In May of 1961, President John F. Kennedy told the world that the United States had some ambitious plans for space. A program was being established, he said, to try to accomplish the greatest engineering challenge ever undertaken by man—reaching the moon. He thought this could be done by 1970.

The idiotic race to the moon! That's what Project Apollo was called by some who argued that the huge sums of money required for the Apollo program could find much better use elsewhere. Others said that America shouldn't pour billions into a moon race with the Soviet Union in an attempt to build world scientific prestige. But in spite of the opposition and certain understandable misgivings, the Apollo program slowly ground forward.

To determine the launch-vehicle requirements for the leap to the moon, engineers first found it necessary to define the Apollo profile—that is, just how was it going to transport three astronauts to the moon and return them safely? It was immediately apparent that a launch vehicle much larger than any of those of the Saturn I family would be required. There were a number of proposals for the new booster, but those finally selected were a series of vehicles called Saturn C-2 through C-5. (The C-1 was the first version of the Saturn I.)

The Saturn C-2 configuration suggested using the basic

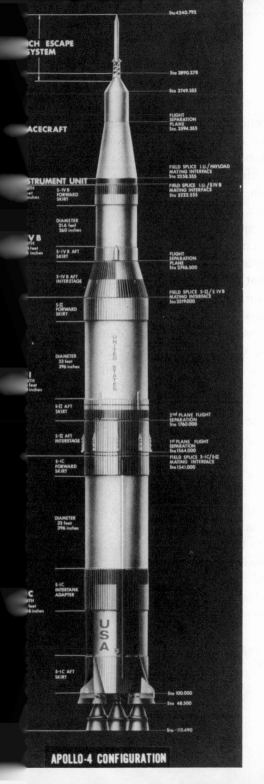

The Saturn V launch vehicle with its Apollo payload.

Courtesy NASA

Saturn I booster, but replacing the 90,000-pound-thrust S-IV second stage with one of a larger diameter powered by a cluster of 200,000-pound-thrust J-2 engines. The Saturn C-3 went one step farther, proposing the complete replacement of the Saturn I first stage with one powered by a new 1,500,000-pound-thrust F-1 engine. Almost unbelievably, the thrust of this new engine would equal or surpass Saturn I's total thrust produced by eight H-1 engines.

After careful consideration of each of these new configurations, it was decided that the proposed rockets just didn't appear to have the necessary performance ability to accomplish the manned lunar mission. So yet another configuration, the C-4, evolved off the drawing boards, one that far surpassed in both size and power the previous C-1 through C-3 configurations. Nestled in the base of the C-4 would be four F-1 engines which could generate a fantastic total thrust of 6,000,000 pounds. The C-4 vehicle also was the first to vary from the basic diameter size of the C-1 class vehicles.

In 1962 the Saturn C-5, a name later to be shortened to Saturn V, was born by adding an additional F-1 engine to the first stage of the C-4 vehicle, thus raising the lift-off thrust value to the 7,500,000 figure. The influence of the Peenemunde scientists was still quite in evidence as all the new vehicles continued to utilize the proven liquid propellants. Actually, if one were to examine the entire space launch vehicle program up to 1962, he would notice that liquid-propellant boosters were used exclusively. However, this trend recently was changed in the Titan IIIC, which, with 2,400,000 pounds of thrust, is powered at lift-off by two 120-inch solid-fuel motors.

Probably the main reason that the engineers shied away

72

from using solid propellants in the Saturn V was the low efficiency they demonstrate. In order to perform as well as the liquid systems, the all-solid-fuel stage would have to be larger and heavier. This added weight, of course, would require more thrust. However, the simplicity and flexibility of solid-fuel motors will certainly enable them to play an important part in the design of future large launch vehicles. Large solid-fuel motors with diameters of 120, 156 and 260 inches are all currently receiving considerable attention.

The large payload capability of the Saturn V could allow the United States moon mission to be accomplished with a single vehicle. Early proposals had suggested a technique known as earth orbit rendezvous (EOR), in which two separate vehicles would be launched to support the single mission. The second vehicle could be launched so that when it reached orbit, it would be near the first. By a series of orbital maneuvers, the vehicles would then be hooked together. This "rendezvous" technique was successfully demonstrated during the two-man Gemini program, when Gemini 10 was attached to an earlier launched Agena target rocket. The advantage of the EOR technique is that smaller launch vehicles could be used, as their payloads would be joined in orbit. This joining effectively accomplishes the same result as a single large launch vehicle.

The technique that was finally decided upon in 1962 was the lunar orbit rendezvous (LOR), which eliminated the complicated earth orbital maneuver required by the EOR idea. The LOR involves boosting the payload to a 100-nautical-mile parking orbit, a task that would be accomplished by using the first two stages of the Saturn V plus a partial burn of the third stage. The third stage, having injected the Apollo payload into the parking orbit, would be shut down and allowed to coast for somewhat less than a complete orbit around the earth. When conditions were exactly right, engineers would reignite the third stage, whose task it would be to add about 10,500 feet per second velocity to the payload and send it on its way to the moon.

Of course, the weight of the Apollo payload is an important factor in the design and performance of the Saturn V rocket. For the Apollo payload to accomplish its task of placing three astronauts on the moon and returning them, it is estimated that the payload would have to weigh a whopping 100,000 pounds. The still-to-be-born Saturn V must be able to give this 50-ton payload an actual velocity of 36,500 feet per second. In reality, though, the Saturn V will also have to be capable of a velocity of an additional 5000 feet per second because two physical factors—drag and gravity—will retard the forward motion of the rocket on its dash to the moon.

The greatest retarding factor during a rocket-powered vehicle's flight is the earth's gravity. The first stage will be most affected by these gravity losses, which will be as much as four times greater for this stage than for the upper stages. As the first stage burn period occurs through the lowest and densest portions of the earth's atmosphere, this stage will also experience the largest drag losses, although they are by comparison are quite small. As a general rule, the gravity losses and the drag losses increase as the initial thrust-to-weight ratio of the particular stage decreases. This is because in the case of the first stage the vehicle remains longer in the lower atmosphere. The size of losses for the upper stages is much lower, but gravity, even with its pull decreased, is still the main consideration. Drag losses are quite small at the higher altitudes because of the thinness of the earth's atmosphere there.

Outwardly, the Saturn V can be described as a two-step vehicle. This means that there are two different diameters—the 33-foot diameters of the first and second stages and the approximate 21-foot diameter of the third stage. Between the stages are the transition sections, called interstages. Sometimes interstages connect stages of the same diameter, and sometimes of different diameters. The Saturn V has a good example of each type.

The S-IC first stage stretches to the amazing length of 138 feet, much longer than many complete multistage rockets. Even more astounding is its diameter—33 feet. A 100-yard dash could be held at the base of the S-IC stage with the sprinters running around the base slightly less than three times. The S-IC stage can hold about 4,500,000 pounds of the old reliable lox/RP-1 fuel combination, and it takes only about two and one-half minutes for the five giant F-1 engines buried in the base to gulp the stage dry. The aft skirt contains four shrouds to protect the four outboard F-1 engines. On each fin is mounted an aerodynamic fin to help stabilize the vehicle during early flight.

The interstage between the S-IC stage and the S-II second stage consists of two parts. Actually, the interstage breaks into two parts when the staging operation occurs, one portion remaining with the burned-out first stage and the other staying attached to the S-II stage. This second portion of the interstage is jettisoned about twenty seconds after the S-II stage has been ignited.

The 81-foot S-II second stage has less than one seventh of the 7,500,000 pounds of thrust of the S-IC stage, but the

S-II burns about three times longer. The S-II stage uses a single common bulkhead between its lox and liquid hydrogen tanks in order to benefit from the weight savings of this technique. With its five lox/liquid-hydrogen-fueled engines, the S-II stage can carry the payload to near the velocity required for earth orbit.

The weight of the S-II stage plus all the weight above it is greater than the thrust produced by its propulsion system. This situation is brought about because upper stages require longer burn times to acquire the necessary speed. Thus, space engineers would describe a stage such as the S-II as having a lift-off thrust-to-weight-ratio of less than one. Thrust-to-weight ratios of less than one are possible with upper stages, as they are merely adding speed more slowly to that already acquired by the first stage. But this situation would not be possible with the S-IC first stage, because it would not lift off the ground. The S-IC stage's thrust is about one and a quarter times greater than the entire weight of the vehicle it must lift.

Another way to show this would be to say that the vehicle's lift-off force is 1.25 G, with 1 G equaling the force of the earth's gravity. Any vehicle that will be able to accelerate at a value greater than the earth's gravity force will be able to move upward. Needless to say, the S-IC's acceleration does not remain at 1.25 G for its entire burn period. When the vehicle is thrusting, it is fast being lightened as the first-stage fuel is being burned. Thus, the acceleration of the vehicle is increased to 4 or 5 G by the time the first stage has burned out.

When designing a vehicle in which men are going to fly, it is very important to consider how many G's they will experience during the powered portion of the flight. Accelerations greater than 6 G over a long period of time are considered harmful to the astronauts.

The S-IVB stage has two missions to perform in the moon trip. First, it must provide the remaining velocity to insert the Apollo payload into the 100 NM (nautical mile) parking orbit. Second, it must provide the escape velocity to drive the Apollo payload toward the moon, a capability that requires the S-IVB propulsion system to restart itself. The S-IVB stage, which is about 12 feet smaller in diameter than either of the two lower stages, uses the same type of J-2 engine as those found on the S-II second stage. However, only one is used on the S-IVB stage. As is also true on the second stage, the liquid-hydrogen fuel is piped through the liquid-oxygen tank in what is called a standpipe. The S-IVB, which was used on the Saturn IB, was the only flight-proven stage in the Saturn V. This stage was proven for the Saturn V as part of the Saturn IB, which has been launched five times to date.

The S-IVB is topped by a three-foot ring called the instrument unit. Weighing about two tons, this section of the vehicle contains all the guidance and control equipment for the launch vehicle. And last, but certainly not least, on top of the instrument unit is the reason for this whole gigantic vehicle in the first place—the Apollo payload, which will be discussed in detail in later chapters.

As immense as the Saturn V is, there were plans at one time to follow it with a much larger family of vehicles—the Nova. These concepts visualized huge boosters with first-stage thrusts as high as 23,000,000 pounds, which is more than three times that of Saturn V. The Nova, it was believed, would be capable of placing 35-ton payloads on the moon and 70-ton payloads into orbit around the planet Mars. However, the

Nova program has since been dropped, and any near-future missions requiring more payload than that of the Saturn V probably will use uprated versions of the Saturn V. Like its smaller brother, the Saturn I, the Saturn V lends itself quite well to uprating.

The 360-foot Saturn V as presently designed can place about 255,000 pounds into a 100 NM orbit. If, however, the Saturn V were required to perform a mission with a higher orbit, it could do so only at the price of a smaller payload. For example, the Saturn V can place about 75,000 pounds in a 1000 NM circular orbit.

Through 1967 there had been about 3,500,000 pounds of payload placed in earth orbit by all nations. This required about 750 launches—but the present Saturn V could do the task with only 15 launches.

The illustration shows the launch vehicle stepping-stones that have led to the Saturn V. In just twenty years we have advanced from a few carloads of V-2 rocket components at a New Mexico desert test range to the multimillion-dollar Kennedy Spaceport and a launch vehicle—the Saturn V— capable of placing three men on the moon and of returning them. Historians will undoubtedly consider this twenty years of our space program as a thrilling period.

The United States launch vehicle development shows how proven concepts were used over and over until better ideas were devised. One can hardly imagine what a similar chart would look like starting with the Saturn V and stretching twenty years into the future.

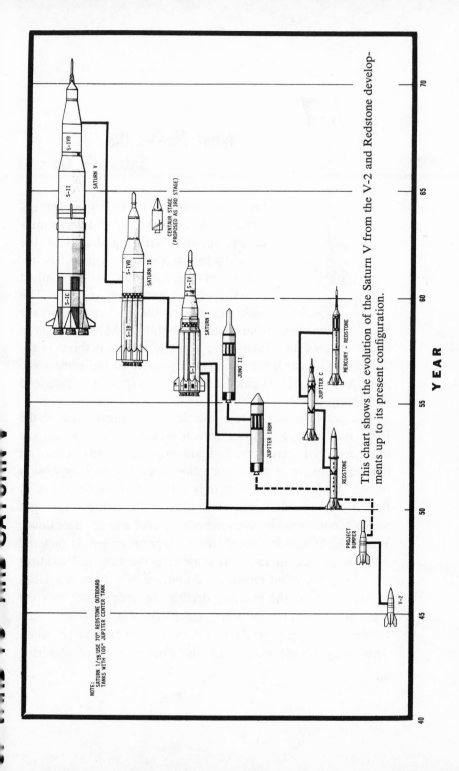

YEAR

NOTE:
SATURN 1/1/B USE 70" REDSTONE OUTBOARD TANKS WITH 105" JUPITER CENTER TANK

This chart shows the evolution of the Saturn V from the V-2 and Redstone developments up to its present configuration.

V-2

PROJECT BUMPER

REDSTONE

JUPITER IRBM

JUNO II

JUPITER C

MERCURY - REDSTONE

SATURN I

S-I

S-IV

SATURN IB

S-IB

S-IVB

CENTAUR STAGE
(PROPOSED AS 3RD STAGE)

SATURN V

S-IC

S-II

S-IVB

7

What Makes the
Saturn V Go

From the early liquid-fueled rocket experiments of Dr. Goddard to today's multimillion-pound thrust liquid engines, the liquid-fueled propulsion system has remained at the forefront of the United States' rapid advancement in space. The main reason for the preference for the liquid engine stems from its high reliability. Although today's liquid engines are much more complicated than those introduced by Goddard, they still employ many of the same basic principles. Liquid engines are of two types—pressure-feed and pump-feed.

The pressure-feed system, the first to be introduced, is the lesser used in today's space launch systems. This type has the three required parts of all liquid engines—a fuel tank, an oxidizer tank, and the combustion chamber and expansion nozzle. However, this system is different from the other in that it has an additional tank filled with high-pressure gas which is connected by lines to both the fuel and oxidizer tanks. When the engine is started, the high-pressure gas is metered into the propellant tanks, thus driving the fuel and oxidizer into the combustion chamber. To ensure flow from the tanks to the chamber, the pressure driving the propellants into the combustive chamber must be greater than that being generated by the exploding propellants within the combustion chamber. This fairly simple system has the disadvantage of requiring

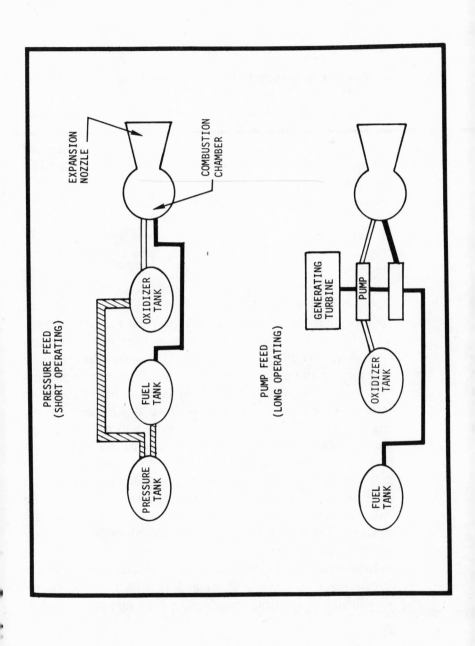

heavy tanks to withstand the high pressure and hence cannot be used on large vehicles. But it has been effectively used on short-range ballistic missiles and surface-to-air guided missiles, such as the Corporal and the Nike.

Although in many ways quite similar to the pressure-feed system, the pump-feed plan uses to advantage a pump to drive the propellants into the combustion chamber. Since the pressure of the pumping system is exerted only between the pump and the combustion chamber, the propellant tanks can be of light construction. This weight-saving advantage is, of course, a most important factor in the design of space launch vehicles.

Liquid propellants for rockets usually consist of an oxidizing agent and a fuel. There are many combinations that can be used, but there are some that are more practical than others. The efficiency of a particular propellant combination is measured by its specific impulse (I_{sp}). Propellants can be united by weight and volume, called "mass mixture ratio" and "volumetric mixture ratios." There is some best mixture in each of these ratios that will produce the highest specific impulse, but other factors must be taken into account before the propellant ratios by weight and volume are selected. A compromise is then made which most effectively takes advantage of all the vehicle characteristics. An example of this compromise is that the best volumetric ratio might require too large a fuel or oxidizer tank and introduce excess weight penalties. The higher I_{sp} produced might not offset the poorer performance brought about by the extra weight.

Liquid propellants are usually classified into three groups— monopropellants, bipropellants and tripropellants. A monopropellant is a chemical compound or a mixture of compounds that are stable at room temperatures but decompose when activated by heat or pressurization. There is only one propellant tank with the monopropellant engine system, but the instability of the fuel prevents its use in large rockets. Bipropellants, the most common combination, are not mixed until they are introduced into the combustion chamber. There, some external source such as a spark plug or another type of igniter will start the burning process. Once the ignition has been started, the firing is continuous as long as the propellants are being forced into the combustion chamber by high-pressure gas or pumps. One class of bipropellants, the hypergolic, burn on contact and thus do not need an igniting device. You can easily imagine the utmost safety precautions which must be observed when this type of propellant is being handled. A tripropellant contains three chemical compounds, with the third serving to improve the performance of the other two.

Thrust is not the only product of the exploding propellant combination. There is also a tremendous heat which splashes against the inside walls of the combustion chamber and the nozzle. So great is the heat that a cooling system must be used to keep the nozzle from burning up. And among the most effective cooling devices is a heat-resistant liner that has worked quite well in short-burn-time engines. But for longer-burning engines, the most effective idea goes back to the method developed by the Germans for the V-2 rocket. Called regenerative cooling, this method circulates the raw fuel around the engine before pumping it into the combustion chamber. With the engine cooled, a longer burn-time is possible. A second advantage of this plan is that as the fuel is being circulated, it is being heated. This preheated fuel then burns more efficiently, with a resulting increase in energy that is released on combustion.

Engine nozzles, which are an important part of the propulsion system of the missile, come in many different shapes and sizes, with the standard cone nozzle resembling an ice-cream cone. The most common nozzle in use is the contoured or bell nozzle. Resembling a hanging bell, this type increases in diameter with a gentle contour to its sides. Many advanced nozzle concepts are now being explored, with the "plug-nozzle" type receiving most attention.

The smallest diameter of an expansion nozzle is called a throat, and the largest is named the exit diameter. The comparison of the two areas of these parts is called the expansion ratio and determines how efficiently the engine will operate at different altitudes. An easy rule of thumb to remember is that engines with low expansion ratios are used in first stages and that engines with high expansion ratios are used in upper stages. Typical expansion ratio values for lower-stage engines would be 10 to 20, while upper-stage values could range as high as 50 to 60.

As explained briefly in another chapter, the Saturn V uses both lox/RP-1 and lox/liquid-hydrogen types of engine systems. However, there are also numerous small solid motors on the vehicle.

The only lox/RP-1 fueled propulsion system on the Saturn V is found in the S-IC first stage, which has five F-1 engines. By far the largest engine on the Saturn V, the F-1 produces more than 1,500,000 pounds of thrust. Actually, one F-1 engine supplies more thrust than the total of the two upper stages. The F-1 uses two shaft-mounted pumps driven by a

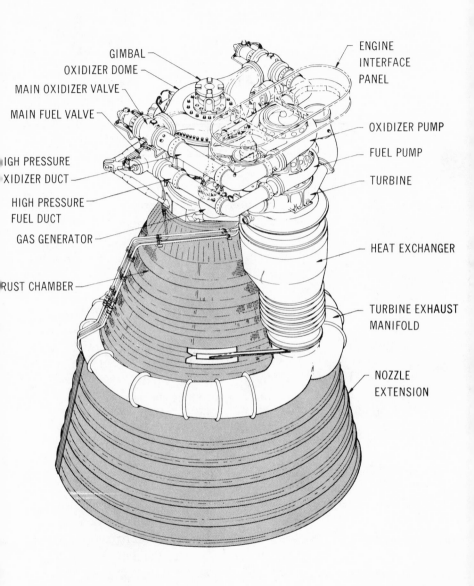

GIMBAL

OXIDIZER DOME

MAIN OXIDIZER VALVE

MAIN FUEL VALVE

IGH PRESSURE
XIDIZER DUCT

HIGH PRESSURE
FUEL DUCT

GAS GENERATOR

RUST CHAMBER

ENGINE
INTERFACE
PANEL

OXIDIZER PUMP

FUEL PUMP

TURBINE

HEAT EXCHANGER

TURBINE EXHAUST
MANIFOLD

NOZZLE
EXTENSION

Courtsey Rocketdyne

F-1 Engine Details

60,000-horse-power turbopump which drives the propellants into the huge combustion chamber. The power of this mammoth pump is equal to that of two hundred automobiles pushing together with throttles wide open. The F-1 has a nozzle extension in order to derive an expansion ratio of 16, and the fairly cool turbine exhaust gases are used to cool this lower skirt.

The five-engine F-1 cluster burns about two and one-half minutes during its portion of the Saturn V powered flight trajectory. The lox oxidizer is fed to the engines through large pipes that pass through the fuel tank. Helium bottles mounted inside the lox tank help to maintain a pressure on the lox. Baffles are located in the base of the lox tank to prevent the oxidizer from sloshing.

The F-1 was a giant step forward from the previous H-1 engine, which generated only 200,000 pounds of thrust. Standing several times taller than the H-1 engine, the F-1 lengthened considerably the lower engine compartment of the S-IC stage. However, when it is realized that forty H-1 engines would have been required to produce the required 7,500,000-pound-thrust figure, the need for a more powerful engine for the Saturn V was obvious.

The F-1 engine, like every other Saturn V part, is always being carefully studied for any improvement that can be made. For instance, Rocketdyne, the F-1 manufacturer and developer, has already proposed a new 1,800,000-pound model that undoubtedly will be used in future Saturn launch vehicles.

The J-2 liquid-hydrogen/liquid-oxygen engine is used on both the second and the third stages of the Saturn V. A highly advanced engine, the J-2 produces a thrust of about 200,000 pounds, and has the extremely high specific impulse of about

Courtesy Rocketdyne

The various components of the highly complicated J-2 engine are shown.

425 seconds. Five of these engines are clustered to form the second-stage propulsion system, while a single J-2 constitutes the propulsion system for the third stage.

In its use with the S-II second stage, the J-2 engines provide a large portion of the speed necessary for the Saturn V to place the Apollo payload into its initial parking orbit. The J-2 engine on the S-IVB third stage provides the thrust required to inject the Apollo payload into an earth parking orbit. And remaining after this "first burn" is a large amount of propellant for use later to push the payload to lunar escape speed. In order to accomplish this last feat, the J-2 must restart in orbit after coasting for less than an orbit.

The very nature of the J-2's propellants presents many problems, the most important of which is that under low gravity conditions the fuel tends to float around inside the tanks. Since this situation makes engine starting difficult, small rockets are used to push the propellants to the bottom of the tanks. This is done during the S-IVB orbital coast phase by allowing liquid hydrogen to vent out and thus exert a slight force on the stage. This has the same effect as the use of the small rockets when the stage is coasting in earth orbit.

For fuel and oxidizer, the J-2 uses separate pumps, each of which is driven by its own turbine. This arrangement permits each pump to be driven at its own selected speed so that the propellant mixture ratio can be changed in flight. The pumps are driven by the hot gas produced by a gas generator.

The J-2 thrust chamber is regeneratively cooled by the extremely cold hydrogen fuel. As the hydrogen fuel performs this cooling function, it becomes a gas, thus allowing it to flow more easily through the cooling jacket. And, of course, the heated liquid hydrogen will be a more efficient fuel when it enters the combustion chamber. The five J-2 engines are mounted in the lower end of the S-II stage in a manner quite similar to that of the first-stage F-1 cluster. That is, there is one center engine with four outboard gimbal-mounted engines. However, the smaller exit diameter of the J-2 permits the cluster to be easily contained within the S-II's 33-foot stage diameter.

Many small solid-propellant rocket motors are also mounted on the Saturn V to perform different tasks. These include motors for separating the vehicle stages, propellant settling and payload escaping.

The separation rockets, commonly called retro-rockets, assure that a lower stage will be significantly slowed after it is separated from the upper portion of the rocket. The retro-rockets prevent the lower stage from crashing into the base of the next-higher-up stage. A collision could easily happen, as you can see, since, when the first stage burns out and separates, it still has about the same speed as the rest of the rocket. The propellant-settling rockets, discussed earlier, provide a force on the fuel to drive it to the bottom of the tanks and make possible easier starting of the engine.

Sitting atop the Apollo payload is the largest Saturn V solid motor, which generates about 150,000 pounds of thrust for eight seconds. This motor provides the means by which three Apollo astronauts could be vaulted away from the Saturn V in case of a launch-pad or early-flight failure. Mounted on a tower structure attached to the top of the Apollo Command Module, this motor has the force to drive the spacecraft high into the air and about a mile away from the vehicle. There are also two other small motors which are part of the "emergency escape system." One is a small 2,850-pound-thrust pitch motor, mounted in the forward portion of the escape system, which tips the spacecraft into an arching flight to keep it out of the path of the Saturn V. The other, the "tower jettison motor," whose two nozzles generate 32,000 pounds of thrust, clears away the entire escape tower in normal flight during the second-stage burn period. This is what the phrase "tower jettison" means when a Saturn V launch is being described.

With its task as precise and demanding as it is, the Saturn V, including all its parts, must work exactly as designed. It hardly needs to be pointed out that the reliability of the propulsion systems is of first importance, since an engine failure means a mission failure. Building reliability into the Saturn V's engines begins with the first design and continues throughout its manufacturing program. Even though each of the main engines generates many thousands of pounds of thrust, it takes only the failure of a ten-cent part, such as a wire or other connector, to stop the engine cold.

The best way to test the dependability of an engine is actually to fire it before it is attached to the rocket. In this manner, the engine can be fired for its full time duration without ever leaving the ground. The testing of a rocket engine is quite different from the testing of an airplane engine. An airplane engine can be tested while the airplane is in the air, and then any mistakes in the building can be corrected on the ground. But with a rocket engine, the engine must operate right the first time or the flight will be a failure.

When a rocket engine is tested on the ground, this action is called a static test. "Static" means stationary or not moving. The structure where this type of test is performed is called a static test stand. A large concrete and steel structure, the stand has one purpose—to hold back the test engine which

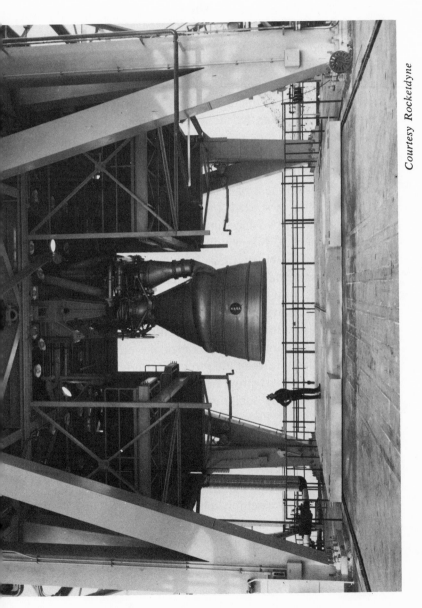

Courtesy Rocketdyne

1,500,000-pound-thrust F-1 engine is mounted in the test stand at Edwards AFB, California.

is trying to thrust itself skyward. The engine is mounted in the test stand with its nozzle pointing down a long exhaust flume into which water is forced while the engine is firing. The water tends to lessen the effect of the searing-hot exhaust gas, thus preventing damage to the flume. The Saturn V's engines are tested both by the manufacturer and by NASA to make doubly sure that they will operate exactly right when the day of flight arrives.

Second only to watching an actual launch is the excitement in seeing the static test of a large rocket engine like the F-1. When the engine is started, the air is shattered with a sound resembling that of two speeding locomotives crashing head-on into each other. A billowing cloud of smoke and steam is hurled skyward as the engine is brought up to full thrust. The deafening sound rumbles across the countryside, shaking windows for miles. But suddenly it is over, and there is silence once more. All that remains is a towering cloud which also will soon vanish. But from these exciting tests the engineers learn every operating characteristic of the engine. Using this information, they are then able to correct any weaknesses.

The F-1 engine test program is carried out in three places —at the Rocketdyne facilities at Canoga Park, California; at the Edwards Air Force Base, California; and at the Marshall Space Flight Center, Huntsville, Alabama. At Edwards the final acceptance testing on the engine is performed to see that all government specifications have been met. Once this testing has been completed, the engines are shipped to the sprawling Michoud assembly plant in Louisiana, where they are mated with the S-IC first stage.

J-2 engine testing is done by Rocketdyne at both Canoga Park and at Santa Susana, California. The Marshall Space

THRUST GROWTH

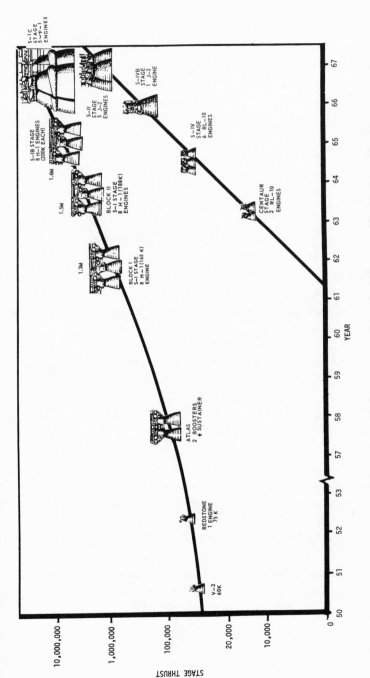

The upper trend line shows the development of lox/RP-1 fueled stages from the 60,000-pound-thrust V-2 to 7,500,000-pound-thrust S-IC. The development of the lox/liquid-hydrogen powered stages is shown by the lower line.

Flight Center also performs tests on the J-2 at Huntsville. Once the J-2 engine tests have been completed, the engines are sent to North American Rockwell's Space Division, where they are attached to the S-II second stage. The McDonnell Douglas Space Systems Center at Huntington Beach, California, also receives J-2 engines for the S-IVB third stage.

As reliable as the engines for the Saturn V are, it should be remembered that they were designed some years ago. And with the advances being made in rocket power, there are numerous changes that now could be made on the engines to improve the overall performance of the Saturn V. But if we waited until every new improvement could be made on the Saturn V, we would be waiting for the moon shot for many years to come.

The Saturn V will undoubtedly see in its lifetime much improvement in its propulsion systems. Already many advanced versions of uprated Saturn V launch vehicles have appeared on the drawing boards with promises of greatly increased performance. Of most interest is the 1,800,000-pound version of the F-1 engine which would raise the total lift-off to 9,000,-000 pounds. Work is also in progress on an advanced version of the J-2 engine which could throttle itself down to extremely low thrust, thus enabling it to be used for maneuvering in space. The J-2 engine of the future will also be greatly simplified. The strap-on technique, already explained, also may be used advantageously on the Saturn V. Large gains in payload can be accomplished by strapping on solid motors or more liquid-fueled propulsion systems.

All of the changes mentioned so far have been possible improvements to the lower stages. However, as even more ambitious future space missions evolve during the 1970's and the 1980's, upper-stage propulsion systems will also require greater efficiency. One low-thrust propulsion system that will provide a specific impulse two to three times greater than that of current chemical rocket engines is the nuclear engine. The 55,000-pound-thrust Nerva nuclear engine is the first step in testing the use of such a power plant. An engine of this type could well find its way into a nuclear-powered Saturn V interplanetary stage which would be launched from an earth parking orbit.

The first ten years in space have produced truly remarkable progress in rocket technology. Single-engine thrust has risen twentyfold from the early Redstone class engines to the awesome 1,500,000-pound F-1. There has also been steady improvement in the liquid-hydrogen engines, which have pushed specific impulse values to well over 400 seconds. This development came about through development of the RL-10 and J-2 engines.

The development of any new rocket engines, be they for improving the Saturn V or for an entirely new space rocket, will undoubtedly depend on which course in space we plan to take following the Apollo moon program—a large orbiting space station, manned exploration of the universe, or a manned moon base.

8

From Drawing Board
to Cape Kennedy

The development of the Saturn V is truly a nationwide program with companies, both large and small, in every part of the nation contributing machine power and, most important of all, manpower. Although the three stage contractors have the major responsibilities, the task of bringing all the parts together is a demanding one. The complete rocket emerges when the stages are brought together for the first time at the launch site at Cape Kennedy.

Because of the size of the Saturn V, the facilities required for assembly and test had to be specifically designed. Also of great importance is the location of these facilities. The main criterion in this selection is access of the facility to a navigable waterway, as barging the Saturn V's first two stages is the best way of transporting them. The third stage can be carried by air.

In a complete look at the Saturn V we might as well start at the bottom with the S-IC first stage, built by Boeing. Being the largest of the Saturn V's powered stages, the S-IC, of course, requires the largest assembly plant, the Michoud operations, located fifteen miles from downtown New Orleans. Before NASA's selection of Michoud in late 1961, the plant had been idle since 1953, when it was used for the manufacture of tank engines. During World War II, plywood cargo planes had been built there. Needless to say, a building re-

Five F-1 engines are installed in the S-IC stage at NASA's Michoud operations in New Orleans.

maining vacant for that length of time would require an extensive amount of repair and change to accommodate the S-IC..

The first thing that had to be done was to strengthen the floors to make them capable of supporting great weights. Some of the engineers who were present when the plant was first reopened found that it was not as uninhabited as had been assumed. The place was absolutely teeming with snakes, many measuring more than six feet, and one of the first tasks was to clear the place of its slithery creatures. Even after the manufacturing operations got under way, many of the workers thought it wise to stay on the sidewalks to avoid the snakes. Thus, it was in rather strange surroundings that the engineers began to assemble the world's largest booster.

The Michoud plant is laid out so that everything flows with great efficiency, with a minimum of confusion. Everywhere you look there are wide aisles which make quite easy the movement of large booster parts throughout the plant. The entire plant is kept amazingly clean.

There is a tooling area in the plant which contains facilities for welding, cleaning and coating the parts which arrive at the loading dock. The 33-foot rings used in the S-IC are turned on a lathe originally used for battleship gun turrets. Final assembly of the S-IC's fuel tanks and joining of the major parts occur in the Vehicle Assembly Building. This huge eighteen-story structure uses an overhead crane to stack the five large tankage sections into a vertical position. The plant is operated jointly by Chrysler and Boeing. (Chrysler builds S-IB first stages for the Saturn IB.)

After the five F-1 engines are installed the S-IC is moved to the Stage Test Building to undergo a complete checkout,

Courtesy NASA

This sequence of photographs shows the vertical assembly of the S-IC stage within the Michoud assembly facility.

including a simulated firing to test the on-board systems. This latter test includes checkout of all electrical and other mechanical systems. Following completion of assembly operations, the S-IC is loaded onto a barge for a short ride to its next destination—the Mississippi Test Operations, where its five engines will be test-fired.

The Mississippi Test Operations, located near Gainesville, Mississippi, is the second large NASA facility in the New Orleans area. This facility, along with the Michoud plant, is under the direction of the Marshall Space Flight Center, which has overall responsibility for the development of space launch vehicles. Located only thirty-eight miles from the Michoud plant, Mississippi Test Operations is responsible for the live testing of the Saturn V's first two stages.

The area chosen by NASA to test the powerful rocket stages has a rich French history dating back to the early 1700's. It was to this quiet spot that NASA came to produce some of the loudest sounds ever heard by man. NASA purchased 13,500 acres of land on which to build the huge static stands for the testing of the rocket stages. Also acquired were 128,000 acres of buffer land, an area directly affected by the rocket-produced sound waves.

Since Gainesville, Logtown and three other small towns in the area were situated within the NASA land mass, it was necessary to relocate them. Houses that were worth moving were rolled away, but all else was leveled. In the relocation, some stray farm stock, mostly cattle and pigs, actually went back to the wild. The cattle, returning to the ways of their ancestors, grew curled horns, and the stray pigs started growing razorbacks. They had learned to live without the help of man.

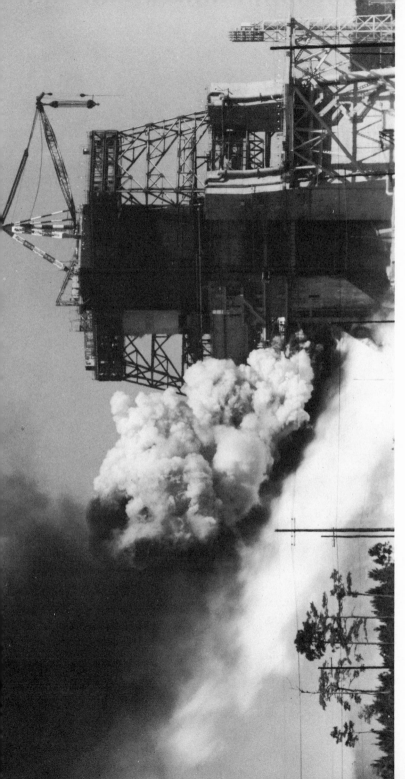

Courtesy NASA

The **S-IC** stage spews flame and smoke as it is static tested on the dual-position **S-IC** stand at the Mississippi Test Facility.

The Mississippi test facility, unlike the Michoud facility, had to be carved from scratch from the lowland. To support the ambitious test program planned for the Saturn V, it was necessary to erect three major complexes, consisting in all of more than sixty buildings. Construction even included the building of a harbor capable of handling barges to carry the rocket stages and propellants. Most visible through the entrance gate are the three large test stands jutting skyward. Two of these are used to test the S-II second stages, while the third is a dual position stand used for testing the S-IC first stage. Even though the facilities are managed by NASA, the checking is actually done by the civilian contractor-builder whose stage is under test.

The static stands for testing a complete stage are, as might be expected, much larger than those used for testing a single engine. Sturdy steel beams hold the stage securely in place while the live firing is in progress. When the S-IC stage is test-fired, the exhaust is forced downward through a curved duct, known as the flame bucket. This bucket directs the exhaust upward slightly into the air, so that very little, if any, of the flame touches the ground. Following completion of their static test, the S-IC stages are loaded onto special barges and shipped to Cape Kennedy for launch.

Designed with the future in mind, the large Mississippi facilities will be able to test the Saturn V follow-on boosters of the 1970's and the 1980's. Although the expense of building these facilities runs high, rocket stages can be tested in them without losing the stages. And these facilities help to cut down the number of live launches required in the test program.

The S-II second stage is manufactured by North American

Rockwell's Space Division at Los Angeles. The assembly process consists of mating four basic subassemblies to form the stage. These assemblies include the aft skirt and thrust structure, the lox tank incorporating the common bulkhead, the hydrogen tank and the forward skirt. Another important part of the S-II structure is the 60-foot tunnel on the outside of the liquid-hydrogen tank, where all electrical wiring is routed between the forward and aft sections of the stage. North American also manufactures the S-IC/S-II interstage, with a diameter of 33 feet, which houses the five J-2 engines and connects the S-II to the S-IC.

Next, following assembly completion, comes a long boat ride for the S-II stage down the California coast, through the Panama Canal, into the Gulf of Mexico and finally to New Orleans and the Mississippi Test Operations. At the testing grounds the S-II stages are checked out, and fired on one of the two S-II stands. Then it's back to the boat again for another long journey, this one to the launch site at Cape Kennedy.

The S-IVB third stage, produced by the McDonnell Douglas Company at its Huntington Beach and Santa Monica plants, is tested completely on the West Coast. While many of the parts for the stage are manufactured by various Douglas plants in the general area, the main assembly operations are concentrated at the Huntington Beach facility.

The S-IVB third stage is quite similar to the one on which it rests in the complete Saturn V vehicle. You could say that the S-IVB is a scaled-down S-II. The S-IVB uses the same liquid-oxygen/liquid-hydrogen propellants and the same J-2 engine system, and is constructed the same way. It has the same basic parts—an aft skirt, a hydrogen tank, a lox tank and the forward skirt assembly. The cone-shaped aft interstage connects the S-II and the S-IVB stages. In flight, this interstage structure is jettisoned with the S-II stage after the latter burns out.

Final assembly of the S-IVB stage is accomplished in several steps. Sections of the propellant tank are welded together in a specially designed tower. Insulation is then placed inside the liquid-hydrogen tank so as to lower the hydrogen boil-off to an acceptable point when the stage is fueled. Eight helium spheres are placed inside the lox tank to pressurize the liquid oxidizer. Following these installations, the forward and aft skirts are installed, along with the thrust structure upon which will be mounted the J-2 engine system. A check-out tower is the scene for the final equipment and engine installation, after which a complete stage test short of actual firing of the engine is conducted. The stage is then shipped to Sacramento, where static tests on the S-IVB propulsion system are carried out.

Two 150-foot static test stands at Sacramento enable all of the S-IVB stages to be thoroughly test-fired to assure that they will operate correctly when they are called on to do so. The S-IVB second stages used for the Saturn IB vehicles go through the same basic assembly and test procedure. However, there are minor changes made to allow interfacing with the S-IB stage and to make possible the different role it plays with the Saturn IB. Following completion of its test program, the S-IVB is shipped to the Cape Kennedy Spaceport in a specially configured aircraft.

Mounted directly on top of the S-IVB stage is the instrument unit (IU), the nerve center of the Saturn V. The IU, 36 inches high and 260 inches in diameter, contains the electronic guidance and control systems for directing the flight of the launch vehicle during its entire powered trajectory. The completely self-contained inertial guidance system within the instrument unit automatically senses errors in the trajectory and issues commands for correction. This is a continuous process during the three basic phases of the trajectory—powered flight through the earth's atmosphere, powered flight in space and coast period in orbit.

The instrument unit is manufactured by the IBM Corporation at its plant at Huntsville, Alabama. Assembly begins by splicing together three curved sections to form the outside of the cyclindrical section. The guidance components, mounted on the inside of this metal ring, include heat exchangers, pumps and a maze of plumbing and electrical wiring bundles. Weighing only 420 pounds after the first curved sections are joined, the instrument unit weighs more than 4000 pounds after all of its equipment has been installed. The IU is the only major piece of flight hardware produced in Huntsville, home of the overall control of the Saturn V—the Marshall Space Flight Center.

In Huntsville, MSFC maintains close supervision over the assembly/test facilities at the Michoud plant, the Mississippi Test Operations, and the in-house facilities of the stage contractors. There are, however, significant rocket test facilities at Huntsville which enabled MSFC to participate actively in the Saturn I static test programs.

The first five S-I first stages were assembled at MSFC before the Michoud plant was ready. The final five S-I stages and all of the Saturn IB first stages were built at the Michoud plant. Facilities at the Marshall Center allowed the testing of the Saturn boosters to begin approximately one year earlier than they could have been had NASA waited for the completion of the Mississippi facilities. The research and development nature of the MSFC stands will enable them to be used in the testing of the next generation of launch vehicles.

Another part of the rocket work at Huntsville is that of the Arm Farm. This area has an exact replica of each of the service arms of the umbilical tower used to service the Saturn V when it is in the launch position at Kennedy Spaceflight Center. The Arm Farm has two functions—checking the operation of the service arms and testing the Saturn V's fit on the launch pad.

Along with performing its overall direction, MSFC has other important functions in supporting the Saturn V program. For instance, many laboratories are busy conducting basic research for improvement of launch vehicles. Much of the research work directed by MSFC is done by civilian aerospace contractors who have come by the dozen to this once-little southern town.

But Huntsville is no longer small. Its population has doubled many times since the Saturn birds arrived. A new research park has sprung up in Huntsville, where many of the Saturn contractors have constructed elaborate new buildings. Where once there were cotton fields, there are now spanking new computers and acres of parking lots. However, during 1962 and 1963, when the influx of workers into the area had just started, the contractors were hard pressed to find the amount of space needed for their large engineering operations. Boeing and Chrysler started work in a hurriedly renovated former cotton mill. The day work started, there were still bales of cotton scattered around the building.

One of the interesting parts of MSFC is the Space Orientation Center, which provides a living history of America's adventure in space. Included are displays of the F-1 and J-2 engines, space capsules and reentry vehicles.

A unique type of work at MSFC is that of dynamic ground testing, which determines the bending and vibration characteristics of the entire rocket. A launch vehicle is not a rigid structure; nor is it an elastic one. It consists of a combination of fluid propellants and of metals of different thicknesses. The loads on the rocket and the characteristics of the rocket change quite rapidly as the fuel is depleted during flight.

The best method of proving how the rocket will react in flight is to place the entire vehicle in the Dynamic Test Stand. This is the only occasion, aside from the time the rocket is placed on the launch pad, that the entire vehicle will be completely assembled. Within this large metal stand the entire rocket can be shaken to determine its flight strength.

The rocket used in the dynamic test program closely approximates that of the actual flight vehicle, both structurally and in weight. Weights are substituted for the fuel in order to simulate its weight within the tanks. The vehicle is pinned at the top and bottom, and shaken to determine its characteristic frequency. This technique could be compared to that of tuning a piano string, the only difference being that with the piano string the desired frequency is known and corrections are made to acquire it. In the case of the dynamic test, we are trying to determine only what the frequency of the rocket actually is.

Another type of work on large rocket boosters is that of battleship testing. A battleship stage is the same size as the actual flight stage, but the former is structurally much more rigid. It is from this added strength that this type of testing gets the name battleship. These battleship stages are used in order to check out operational procedures that will be performed on the flight stages, such as fuel loading, propulsion system firing operations and tank and feed operations.

The development of the Saturn V has made necessary a test program of much greater proportions than was carried out for the earlier space boosters. As this rocket will be used to carry men into space, no expense has been spared to ensure all possible reliability. The J-2 engine, which powers the two upper stages of the Saturn V, has been ground-tested about twenty-five hundred times, and the first-stage F-1 engine has been fired up more than three thousand times. It is hoped that through this extensive test cycle even any small defect in design will show itself.

The actual flight rocket also is subjected to inspections, which include looking by X-ray into the seam welds to determine whether any imperfections exist. Cracks appearing in welds have been a source of some trouble in the Saturn V program. A sound-inspection technique, known to the enginees as ultrasonics, is used to check the approximate five miles of tubing in the rocket.

With all this checking and rechecking, it certainly makes one wonder why rocket failures occur at all. There are, however, failures, and undoubtedly there always will be because of the human element involved. But these long inspection and testing periods have rewarded us with an ever increasing success rate in our space launching. For example, not a single one of the Saturn I or Saturn IB launch vehicles has failed to accomplish its mission. This is a truly remarkable accomplishment, one engineers hope can be matched by the much larger and more complicated Saturn V.

The coming of rockets the size of the Saturns has produced

Courtesy NASA

Two NASA barges pass the New Orleans skyline after leaving the Michoud Assembly Facility. The Poseidon, on the left, carries the S-IC stage of the Saturn V.

another problem in addition to that of manufacturing—transportation. How does one move, from one part of the country to another, an object 33 feet in diameter, 150 feet long and weighing 150 tons?

For moving booster stages short distances, about the only way is to use ground transportation, and specially designed trailers have been built for this task. But this type of transportation is very slow and requires an expensive motor cavalcade as an escort to protect the precious cargo. The mere size of the boosters prevents any use at all of the railroads, mostly because of small clearances on bridges and tunnels.

The least expensive and most widely used method of moving parts of rockets is by water. So, availability of navigable water was one of the main reasons for locating the various NASA assembly and test facilities on the Mississippi River or its tributaries. In the case of the early Saturn boosters, which were assembled at Huntsville, the long trip to Cape Kennedy began on the Tennessee River at Huntsville, where the boosters were loaded onto barges with cocoon-type covers. The 2200-mile trip to the Cape required a travel time of about ten days. With the coming of the larger S-IC stages, larger barges, of course, were required.

Typical of the type of barges used by NASA is the Poseidon. The unpowered barge is pushed by a small tugboat. Barges such as this one are a common sight on the Mississippi these days.

There is still another method of moving rocket boosters— by aircraft. In recent years a whole new family of aircraft specifically designed to carry outsized cargo such as the Saturn rocket stages has been born. These new planes have been given the name "Guppy," after the small fish which

Guppy, the first of several different versions, is shown in flight and loading Saturn S-IV rocket stage.

they so closely resemble. Converted from the Boeing C-97 Stratocruiser, the Guppy has been so completely reworked that the diameter of its fuselage is much larger than in its Stratocruiser form. The new aircraft, of which there are several versions, are capable of carrying the smaller stages of the Saturn rockets, namely the S-IV and S-IVB upper stages. The thirty-three-foot diameter of the S-IC and S-II stages so far makes their transport by air impossible, although new versions of this aircraft now being considered might be large enough to handle even these large stages.

SATURN V ASSEMBLY, TEST, & LAUNCH

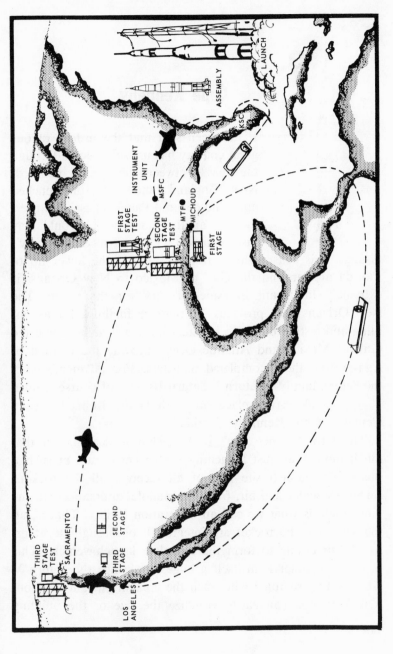

Shown are the locations for the manufacture and test of the three Saturn V stages and the route of transportation to the launch site.

9

Cape Kennedy

It has been said that the history of our great country has unfolded down through the years between the rugged coast of New England and the sun-drenched and sand-covered Pacific coast. However, there is another coast which could play just as important a part in our country's history. This coast, which stretches around the lower tip of Florida and around the Gulf of Mexico to New Orleans, is extremely important in America's try for the moon. The New Orleans area provides the massive facilities for assembling and testing the huge boosters for space flight, while the Gulf of Mexico and Atlantic Ocean provide the method of transporting these completed monsters. For all members of the Saturn family—Saturn I, Saturn IB and, of course, Saturn V—the final resting place on earth is the Kennedy Space Center at Cape Kennedy, Florida.

The term "launch site" is somewhat misleading, in that much more than just launching the rocket occurs at such a place. The launch site first of all receives all the rocket's stages, by water and air, from the manufacturers. Second, the launch site is what we call an integration facility. That is, all the stages of the rocket are integrated, or brought together, for the first time to form the complete launch vehicle. This bringing together is in itself a huge task, since the Saturn V when fully assembled will reach the amazing height of about 370 feet. You can easily visualize the size of the building required to allow this rocket to stand upright within it. The launch site also serves as a check-out facility to assure that once the vehicle has been assembled, all components promise to work as one.

Another task to be performed is the transporting of the complete vehicle to the launch pad. Arrival at the launch pad signals the last earth-bound movement the Saturn V will make. Activity at the launch pad consists of propellant loading and still more testing. It goes without saying that the buildings and equipment required to fulfill the many functions of the Saturn V launch site had to be specially designed for that purpose. The facilities that have resulted are almost beyond imagination, overshadowing many times over any of the previous launch facilities.

The operations we have just described are carried out on the Saturn V at an area within the Kennedy Space Center known as Launch Complex 39, located at Merritt Island, just east of Titusville, Florida. Launch Complex 39 is divided into six major areas, each of which performs a separate important function. In order to understand how each of these areas operates, let's follow a rocket from the time it arrives at the Cape until the launch button is pressed.

As stated earlier, the two largest lower Saturn V stages will arrive by barge, while the third stage, the instrument unit, and the payload will arrive by Guppy aircraft. The barges will be moored at the end of a canal quite close to a large structure known as the Vehicle Assembly Building (VAB). Since all of the booster stages are resting horizontally on the barge decks, they can be towed easily on carriers to the pier and into the VAB.

With the tallest part standing about 525 feet, the VAB

is the second-largest building in the world. It would be possible to place any of the world's other large buildings inside the VAB, and there would still be plenty of room to spare. The VAB is strong, too. It was built to withstand winds of up to 125 miles per hour, a requirement for a geographical location which has seen its share of hurricanes in the past.

There are two basic areas within the VAB—a high bay and a low bay. The low bay area contains the necessary shops and equipment for preparing the upper stages and the instrument unit. This area has eight check-out cells in order to accomplish this work. The high bay area is used to erect and check out the S-IC and to mate it with the rest of the launch vehicle. As the high bay is more than 500 feet high, it can easily accommodate the overall height of the complete Saturn V. In order to work on the rocket while it is in vertical position, air-conditioned work platforms at several different levels completely encircle the vehicle. The high bay area also has the capacity to hold four Saturn V rockets simultaneously.

In order to accomplish the many tasks, there are more than 140 cranes and other lifting devices located within the VAB ranging in size from the small one-ton hoists to the 250-ton bridge cranes. The high bay area has four 450-foot doors to allow movement of completed Saturn V vehicles from the VAB to the launch pad. Upon entering the VAB, you take on the proportions of an ant crawling in a giant world of oversized equipment and gigantic structures. Standing on one of the upper levels of the building makes one aware that this building was designed to perform a monumental task, and indeed it was.

When the Saturn V leaves the VAB, it will be completely checked out and ready to be installed on the launch pad. This testing will reduce to a minimum the time required for the rocket to remain on the pad before launching.

Located just southwest of the VAB and connected to the VAB by an overhead passageway is the Launch Control Center (LCC), the electronic brain of Launch Complex 39. This building serves many functions during the rocket assembly processes in the VAB, and also controls the Saturn V countdown and launch. Within the LCC is one of the most advanced check-out systems ever conceived by man. Programed test sequences contained in an LCC computer are transmitted to another computer on the vehicle's mobile transporter. These tests will then be administered to the rocket, the results of which will provide a "GO" or "NO GO."

Within the LCC are a maze of monitors which operators carefully scan to catch the slightest inkling of any defect of the rocket. Many monitors contain television screens which provide an on-the-spot look at any item of concern. There are also several hundred voice communication links from the crew to the director to keep him abreast of all the latest developments as the countdown progresses.

The Saturn V incorporates a whole new idea in operations at Launch Complex 39 with what is termed the mobile launcher. This contraption is the largest vehicle ever to ride on tracks in the world. The launcher is in effect a movable platform incorporating an umbilical tower on its half-acre top surface. Standing about 450 feet above ground level, the tower and the base section are exerting a force of more than 11,000,000 pounds on the four tracked units of the crawler.

The best way to describe the mobile launcher with Saturn V aboard is to imagine the Washington Monument mounted on a twenty-foot-thick slab of steel the size of a football field.

This monstrous load is then placed atop four huge trackers, the tread cleats of which weigh about a ton apiece. Visualize now this massive hulk of steel approaching down a super-highway, completely straddling both lines of traffic and the grass median strip. This gives some idea of how the Saturn V atop the mobile launcher looks on its trip to the launch pad.

The transporter, 130 feet long and 114 feet wide, moves on four high double-tracked crawlers. Power for the transporter is provided by two diesel engines generating a total of 5300 horsepower, or about that of 26 automobiles. The 5,500,000-pound transporter must carry its 11,000,000-pound load about three miles, from the Vehicle Assembly Building to the launch pad, the last part of the journey including 5 percent grade incline. The whole trip from the VAB to the launch pad takes about ten hours.

The Saturn V, when it is being carried by the transporter, must be kept in an exact vertical position at all times. And in order to accomplish this delicate task, there are a series of manual and automatic leveling devices which are a part of the transporter. Probably the largest land vehicle ever built, the transporter is allowed only a two-inch tolerance in positioning itself at the VAB and at the launch pad.

Many difficulties were experienced when the crawler first started making trial runs on an asphalt-topped roadway. The tremendous weight caused the asphalt to roll up like a carpet, with huge chunks of the material sticking between the cleats of the crawler. The remedy, surprisingly, was to use a special crushed rock mixture. It certainly appears strange to see a "secondary" gravel road in a modern space complex such as LC 39. But it is estimated by NASA that the road will support up to 18,000,000 pounds. Of course, the rocks are considerably smaller after the crawler has rolled over them, in some cases reducing them almost to powder. The giant cleat depressions left by the crawler in the roadway resemble those of some ancient dinosaur.

Mounted directly on the crawler, the launch base consists of approximately 1200 feet of floor space within its three levels. The upper level, in addition to the umbilical tower, contains four rocket hold-down arms, and the two lower levels have a large number of work compartments. There is also a hole 45 feet in diameter—12 feet larger in diameter than that of the Saturn V—to accommodate the exhaust from the S-IC stage at launch. The launcher base is built so that it can be attached to the crawler, to mounting mechanisms within the VAB and also to six pedestals located at the launch pad.

The most significant feature of the mobile launcher is the umbilical tower. This giant open steel structure, mounted on the launcher base, provides the support for a maze of servicing equipment, among which are eight service arms, one access arm, and numerous electrical and pneumatic subsystems. A 250-foot crane is mounted atop the tower that stretches over the Saturn V when it is in place. The service arms extending from the umbilical tower provide access to the vehicle and contain the necessary service lines to the vehicle while it is on the launch pad.

Once the mobile transporter has arrived at the launch pad, it will leave most of its load there. The launcher base will be installed on the pedestals of the pad, and the crawler will be detached and then moved away. But its job is not done yet; it will have to be used again before the rocket is launched.

The uppermost service arm, which provides access to the command module of the Apollo payload, can be controlled from the LCC. In normal operation, it is retracted thirty minutes before launch; however, it can be quickly extended in case of an on-pad emergency to allow the on-board astronauts to leave the rocket quickly. The second service arm is connected to the service module of the payload. The other seven service arms are all connected to various portions of the launch vehicle.

Four hold-down arms support the vehicle during the various operations from assembly through launch. These hold-down arms keep the rocket on the launch pad until the proper thrust has been obtained. The rocket is actually held for about five seconds after the five F-1 first-stage engines have been ignited. If one or more of the engines fail to ignite, or are not producing the full thrust, the vehicle is not released by the hold-down arms, and the engines are all shut down. This type of operation was demonstrated during the Gemini Program when, on one launch attempt, the Titan II booster was shut down on the pad after the booster had failed to generate full first-stage thrust.

The mobile launcher with its crawler, launcher base and umbilical tower is truly a versatile piece of space-age equipment, being involved with rocket operations through assembly, transfer to the pad, pad installation and, finally, launch. Although appearing quite cumbersome, this machine has pointed the way for launch operations for vehicles many times larger than the Saturn V.

Following its job of placing the launcher base on the pad, the crawler-transporter carries the large "mobile service structure" to the pad where, opposite the umbilical tower, it encircles the rocket. The purpose of the structure, as its name indicates, is to service the rocket and the Apollo payload

Courtesy NASA

The Saturn V, atop its mobile launcher, leaves the Vehicle Assembly Building on its way to the launch pad.

while it is on the pad. Five work platforms provide the engineers and technicians access to the Apollo. Electrical power, air conditioning, fire protection and fueling devices are but a few of the many different types of equipment available on the mobile service structure. During periods when no launch operations are under way, the service structure is parked a mile away from the pad. More than 400 feet tall, the service structure is removed from the pad several hours before launch.

The launch pad itself is a massive concrete structure which provides the base for the mobile launcher and the system for riding the flames and exhaust gases. The launch site, with its eight sides, is more than half a mile wide. There is a deep trenchlike opening, cutting most of the way across the pad, to carry the flaming exhaust away from the pad area and hold to a minumum the damage to the pad and equipment. Located in the center of the flame trench and placed directly under the base of the Saturn V's base section is a wedge-shaped object called a flame deflector. The deflector is the first item that will feel the scorching exhaust heat of the F-1 engines as they are brought to life. The exhaust gases are then swept down the curved portion of the deflector and on out the flame trench.

An elaborate water cooling system, similar to but smaller than that of the static test stand, is used to cool the exhaust gases. More than 40,000 gallons of water can be pumped through the cooling pipes every minute. In the test stand, the stage or engine being tested is held in position during its entire firing period and thus generates much more heat than in actual launching, when the rocket is on the pad only a few seconds.

Once the Saturn V is resting safely on the pad, it must be

Courtesy NASA

Apollo 6, the second Saturn V launch vehicle, rests atop its mobile launcher at Pad A, Launch Complex 39.

fueled. Different portions of the rocket are fueled at different times during the launch countdown. Propellant loading for the propulsion systems of the spacecraft is done before launch day. The propellants for the third-stage control system are also tanked at this time.

Located near LC 39 are the necessary storage facilities for the propellants, which for the Saturn V are liquid oxygen, RP-1 fuel and liquid hydrogen. The facility can store 900,000 gallons of liquid oxygen, while the RP-1 facility has three 86,000-gallon tanks. The liquid hydrogen facility, which supplies the Saturn V's two upper stages, has a storage capacity of about 850,000 gallons.

Fueling operations for the S-IC stage are started one day before the launch when the RP-1 fuel is pumped aboard. However, owing to the boil-off problems associated with liquid oxygen and liquid hydrogen, these fuels are not loaded until seven hours before launch time. The liquid oxygen loading is started first in the precooled tank of the second stage. The stage is filled only to about half its capacity, and this is followed by a complete loading of the S-IVB third stage. The S-II stage loading is then completed, and this operation is followed by the complete filling of the S-IC first stage. The reason for this rather irregular loading sequence is to enable the S-II stage to be checked for any leaks prior to complete filling. The liquid hydrogen fueling operations take place last, with the S-II stage being completely filled first. The fueling operation for both the oxygen and hydrogen takes about four and one-half hours.

As the fully loaded Saturn V rocket sits on the pad it holds within its fuel tanks more than 5,500,000 pounds of propellants. If the fueled rocket were to explode on the pad, there would be a force equal to about 600 tons of TNT. Extreme care is therefore taken during the loading operations and in activities when the vehicle is in the fueled condition.

If a minor accident should occur when there is a fully fueled Saturn V on the pad, the three Apollo astronauts would be able to leave the rocket by a high-speed elevator and personnel chute. If the danger were serious, the spacecraft's launch escape rocket would be activated and the crew would be tossed away from the rocket. But for less hazardous conditions, such as propellant leaks, the elevator and personnel chute would be used. The first leg of the escape route, after the men had left the spacecraft and had sprinted across a service arm, would be on the high-speed elevator, located in the adjacent umbilical tower, which would bring them to the base of the tower. At this point they would jump into the personnel chute, which would drop them about another hundred feet to a special blast-proof room at the base of the launch stand. It is now estimated that it would require about two and one-half minutes to have the astronauts safely in the blastproof area.

In our discussions thus far about Launch Complex 39, we have talked about each piece of equipment as though there were only one of each. This is not the case. For example, there are two pads at LC 39, Pad 39A and Pad 39B. Both are entirely independent of each other, and operations can be carried out separately on both pads at the same time. For safety reasons, the pads are located about one and one-half miles apart. There are two crawlers transporters and three mobile launchers, but only one mobile service structure.

Although the most exciting part of the activities that are carried on at the Kennedy Space Center is the Saturn V operation at Launch Complex 39, many other activities there are related to both space and missiles. Because Merritt Island is used only in part by Saturn V, a wildlife preserve and citrus groves have been established on the other areas. Consequently, NASA has been able to study the effects on vegetation of fuels and oxidizers which have remained in the lower atmosphere.

The rest of the facilities at the Cape are manned jointly by the Air Force and NASA, with the control being assumed by the Air Force. NASA also has Launch Complexes 34 and 37, which are used for vehicles in the Saturn I family.

The Air Force functions at Cape Kennedy, under the direction of nearby Patrick Air Force Base, have been directly related to offensive ballistic missile development. Many of the early Redstone missiles, along with versions of the Titan and Atlas ICBM's, were fired from this facility. The early Redstone and Atlas-boosted Mercury capsules, the first NASA rockets directly related to the manned space program, were also launched from the Cape. These were followed in turn by the Titan-boosted Gemini two-man capsules. These earlier manned space programs were proving launch concepts which would find their way into the Apollo program at Launch Complex 39.

Probably the most impressive sight at Cape Kennedy is the "gantry row," where launch pads of almost every size and shape are lined up in a long line along the edge of the water. It certainly is a sight not to be missed if you are able to visit the Cape.

10

Ground-Tracking
the Saturn V

Another important facility in the Saturn V program that has not been explained is the vast ground-based electronic tracking network whose job it is to monitor the flight of the rocket from the lift-off until the splash-down of the Apollo payload into the ocean.

The requirements dictated by the Apollo mission will present many problems that were not encountered in the Mercury and Gemini programs. The Saturn V, a much more powerful rocket than either of the other two, injects the Apollo payload into its in initial parking orbit much farther downrange and, therefore, requires more instrumentation. The fact that injection into the lunar trajectory could occur over either the Atlantic or Pacific Ocean requires that monitoring equipment be placed at both locations. Since the final goal for the Apollo is the moon, 250,000 miles away, extremely accurate deep-space tracking equipment is required.

The ground-based Apollo support structure has three parts —launch, orbital and interplanetary phases, and reentry. Of course, the prelaunch and launch operations, already described, are under the control of Kennedy Space Center. This control remains at Kennedy through the Saturn V liftoff, until the rocket has cleared the top of the umbilical tower. The control is maintained at the launch site so that immediate abort, or cancellation, action can be taken if an early malfunction should occur.

Many precautions must be taken before the Saturn V launch occurs. The entire downrange area over which the rocket will pass must be completely cleared of all shipping and aircraft traffic, a precaution that is the responsibility of the Range Safety Officer. But probably the most important job of the Range Safety Officer is that of assuring that the vehicle safely clears the launch area. If the rocket should start to deviate from its normal flight or start to break apart, the command destruct system would destroy the vehicle. Command destruct, in doing its work, actually shuts down the first-stage engines and splits open the fuel tanks. This action can be initiated at any time up until the insertion of the payload into earth parking orbit. Of course, before the destruction command is given, the astronauts are blown clear of the rocket by the launch escape system. You can imagine the responsibility that rests with the Range Safety Officer who, with the pushing of a single button, can destroy a Saturn V costing many millions of dollars.

Once the vehicle has successfully passed over the top of the umbilical tower, operational control is transferred to the Manned Spacecraft Center (MSFC) at Houston, Texas. Located in Houston is the Flight Director, who has overall control of all aspects of the mission. Hence, any important change in the basic mission plan must be approved by him.

Once the rocket has risen into the air, it pitches over and arches gracefully out over the Atlantic Ocean. There are two advantages for the vehicle when it takes this easterly direction. First, the rotation of the earth provides the rocket with a running start. The earth is whirling around an imaginary line connecting the north and south poles at a speed of about 1000 miles an hour at the equator. At the Cape, this velocity, reduced to about 850 miles an hour, is in effect "free" speed added to that of the rocket.

However, in order to derive full benefit from this earth rotational velocity at the latitude on which the site is located, the vehicle must be launched in an easterly direction. If the vehicle is launched above or below due east, only a fraction of the earth's velocity can be taken advantage of. Of course, it may not always be possible to fire exactly due east because of some range restriction. The Saturn V is launched at 72 degrees east of north, which is quite close to a due east direction.

When a rocket is launched either due north or due south, it neither benefits nor loses from the earth's rotational velocity. As far as the vehicle would be concerned in these polar launch situations, the earth would be standing still. Firing against the earth's rotation, that is firing west, would penalize the rocket.

The second advantage of the easterly Saturn V launches, and for all Cape Kennedy launches, is that all spent rocket stages will fall harmlessly into the Atlantic Ocean. All other jettisoned items will also meet the same fate. Since the functioning of the stages is recorded by telemetry, it is not necessary to recover the burned-out stages. The location of these stage impact areas can be accurately determined by computer programs, but the areas will vary from flight to flight depending on the nature of the boost profile. The two most important factors affecting the location of the impact points are the angle of the stage and the speed at which it burns out. During the Saturn V's trajectory to earth orbit, both the S-IC and S-II stages will burn out short of orbital velocity and fall back into the water. To give an idea of just how far these stages are projected downrange, the first Saturn V mission, Apollo 4, had a first-stage impact point of 350 miles downrange, and the S-II stage had one of 2100 miles.

The second portion of the Apollo structure includes all the flight portions of the mission to the moon and return. In order to support this flight, NASA and the Department of Defense have assembled a massive network of ground, sea and airborne stations completely encircling the globe. This network forms what is known as the Manned Space Flight Network (MSFN).

The MSFN keeps track of the Apollo spacecraft during its entire lunar mission. When we usually think of the word "tracking," we visualize radar following the movement of an object in space. To the MSFN, however, tracking means establishing a link between the Apollo and the Control Center at the Manned Spacecraft Center. Consisting of many channels transmitting tracking, voice and data, this link provides the only method of communication between the ground and the three Apollo astronauts. Another important function to be provided by the MSFN is that of navigation—no small job in itself.

Although the navigational function could be performed by the Apollo itself, this complicated task can be done much more accurately and easily from the ground. The advantage of the ground-based system comes from the fact that the tracking stations around the world are so carefully located that the precise position of the vehicle at any time during its flight can be accurately determined quite easily and quickly. If the positions were determined on board the vehicle, it would be necessary to do the tedious and time-consuming tasks of sighting and measuring angles between certain stars, planets and the earth.

Each of the downrange tracking sites, miniature electronic facilities in themselves, bristles with sophisticated radar and other electronic devices. These tracking sites, operated for the government by Pan American World Airways, are manned entirely by civilian employees. Each of these sites, small communities in themselves with all the comforts, has a particular time during the flight when it will be the prime monitor. That is to say, the vehicle is passed from site to site as it is followed around the world. As one site loses the vehicle, it comes into range of the next monitor. This tracking information is immediately flashed to Houston, where it is analyzed. This technique is not new, as tracking stations were used to follow ballistic missiles and the early NASA and Air Force space shots. Valuable experience was acquired before the monumental task of tracking the Saturn V and its Apollo payload began.

The global tracking network is vast. In the tracking operation for the first Saturn V launch, Apollo 4, there were thirty-one stations, including sixteen provided by the Department of Defense. These stations consisted of specially outfitted aircraft, seagoing vessels and land installations. The aircraft and seagoing vessels fill the voids that cannot be covered by the land stations. The number of tracking stations will vary with the particular mission being flown.

The range instrumentation ship *General H. H. Arnold,* one of the many vessels that will play a central role in tracking the Apollo, resembles a floating radar station. These ships weigh as much as 22,000 tons and can remain at sea for as long as two months. This latter capacity is absolutely necessary, since in some cases there may be several launch cancellations and holds which could stretch the wait into weeks.

Many of these ships began as transports or tankers, but have since been extensively modified to fulfill their new purpose. As it is important to determine exactly where the events of the mission profile will occur, it is necessary to have as many of these tracking ships as possible located strategically around the world to transmit the information back to Houston. This is the second important use of ships in the Apollo mission. The first was the use of barges to transport the Saturn stages from California and Michoud to Cape Kennedy.

The Apollo Range Instrumentation Aircraft (ARIA) are converted C-135 jet tankers, each equipped with a ten-foot extension known as a "droop snoot." Each of these snoots contains a steerable radar, the largest ever mounted on an aircraft. Weighing almost 140 tons when fully loaded, the ARIA carries a crew of eleven. Along with supporting the space programs of NASA, these aircraft also function in Air Force ballistic missile and space launches. The ARIAs receive and transmit telemetry information from the Apollo spacecraft during parking orbit, transfer into the lunar trajectory and earth reentry.

The ARIAs, based at Patrick Air Force Base, are deployed as much as seven days ahead of launch time so that they can be on station near their area of coverage five days before the countdown. The ARIAs leave their waiting positions from about one to four hours before launch time so as to be located in the exact positions to perform their missions during the flight.

Monitoring the rocket while it is in translunar trajectory is

Courtesy USAF

The range instrumentation ship the *H. H. Arnold.*

as important as tracking the vehicle up to its parking orbit. Tracking is especially necessary during the S-IVB's burn period, which occurs while the vehicle is in parking orbit.

During the Apollo's trip to the moon, it will be necessary to make three midcourse corrections in order to correct the trajectory. These changes will assure that the spacecraft will be inserted into the desired lunar orbit. Once the mission has been completed, the spacecraft will free itself from the lunar orbit and begin its long journey back to earth. Three midcourse maneuvers are also used on the return journey. The ground network, with its long-range tracking radars, is responsible for the ground navigation before and after all of the maneuvers. So sensitive are these radars that they are able to track accurately the relatively small Apollo spacecraft at a distance of almost 250,000 miles into the darkness of space.

All that remains after the spacecraft has returned to the vicinity of the earth is for it to make a safe reentry. At this time the ground-based network has its third and last task to perform. On a normal Apollo reentry trajectory, the spacecraft, as it nears the earth, would fly over China and Japan with the planned impact in the general area of Hawaii. All available ships and aircraft would be in the area to track and later recover the spacecraft during this critical portion of the flight. The Mercury and Gemini programs showed amazing accuracy in landing quite close to the predicted splash-down points.

Now that the Apollo has been delivered safely from the moon and has survived the blazing friction heat from the earth's atmosphere, the last task is the recovery of the astronauts and the module. As the general position of the spacecraft

Courtesy USAF

The Apollo Range Instrumentation Aircraft (ARIA) with the ten-foot "droop snoot."

has been located, it is now the responsibility of the Air Force and Navy to pick up the valuable package bobbing in the warm waters of the Pacific. It has been estimated that a downed spacecraft can be recovered anywhere in the world within eighteen hours. This maximum time should make most recoveries safe, since tests have shown that the Apollo command module is seaworthy for about forty-eight hours.

The primary support for the Pacific recovery of Apollo comes from a task force resting near the expected impact point. Among the equipment to aid in the recovery is an armada of helicopters and aircraft. The choppers carry highly skilled para-rescue jumpers who will be dropped near the floating spacecraft to aid the astronauts. A special flotation collar is also attached to the spacecraft.

There must also be ships and aircraft in secondary landing areas in which the spacecraft could land should termination of the flight be earlier than first planned. One other area where recovery is extremely important is in the general vicinity of the Merritt Island launch area. If there should be an on-pad explosion, it would be necessary for the Command Pilot to initiate the launch escape system. Even when the Saturn V was on the launch pad, the astronauts could be dumped into the ocean. The same recovery procedures employed at the main recovery area would also be used in this emergency.

Since by this time there isn't much left of the first two Saturn V stages, you might think that the spacecraft is the only item to be recovered. But saved also must be two cameras from the S-II second stage, which have photographed the separation of the second stage from the S-IC first stage. Helicopters from an Atlantic ship recover these cameras after they have been jettisoned in protective containers into the sea.

A vast outlay of men, ships and aircraft will be required to track and recover the Apollo spacecraft. But not all of this massive network was built, in the beginning, exclusively for Saturn V/Apollo program. Much of the equipment, though now improved, came from the earlier Mercury and Gemini programs. However, these early programs only scraped the surface of the technology required for the Saturn V/Apollo. Sending a man to the moon will present the greatest challenge ever attempted in space navigation and tracking.

11

The
Apollo Spacecraft

The Saturn V has one purpose—that of propelling the Apollo payload through the heavens. And the Apollo payload is truly an engineering masterpiece, one that is probably more complicated than its Saturn V booster. Of course, while the entire rocket rests on the pad prior to a launch, the launch vehicle and the spacecraft are actually acting as one, each depending on the other for a mission's success.

On earth we take food, air and water for granted. But these necessities are not available in the hostile environment of space, and in order for man to survive, it is necessary to take these materials along. Also, man has evolved on the earth with 14.7 pounds per square inch pressing down on him. Therefore, an atmospheric pressure close to this value must be provided aboard the spacecraft. It is also necessary to provide a temperature that is fairly close to that of a man's body.

While man is in space, he must live in a pressurized container, be it a pressure suit such as was required with the Mercury and Gemini capsules or the shirt-sleeve environment planned for the Apollo spacecraft. The considerable heat generated by the human body and equipment must be continually vented out so that a near constant temperature can be kept within the spacecraft. Since the weight and space that water, food and oxygen take up subtract from the amount of experimental equipment that can be carried, it is especially important to keep these three items to a minimum. In order to accomplish this, some very advanced techniques have been developed by NASA, working with private industry.

One of these procesess is known as regeneration, a method of restoring a material to its original properties after it has undergone a change. For example, when we drink water, it becomes contaminated as it absorbs the waste products of the body. But when passed through a series of specially designed filters, the water can be made pure and usable again. A similar process can be employed for reclaiming the oxygen breathed by the astronauts. As was true with the water, the oxygen is not lost when it is inhaled into the lungs. What happens is that the oxygen is combined with carbon within the body and exhaled as carbon dioxide. By an intricate system of filters, the unwanted portions of the carbon dioxide gas can be extracted, leaving the pure oxygen to be reused time and again. With a system of this type operating at 100 percent efficiency, it is estimated that twenty pounds of oxygen could sustain an astronaut for his entire life.

The fact that there is a zero G, or no gravity, environment within the spacecraft also tends to present problems. The act of eating requires that the food be in tubes and actually squeezed into the mouth in order to prevent it from floating around inside the spacecraft. No fluids can be allowed to encounter directly the environment of the spacecraft, as they would immediately turn into globs and go floating around the interior of the cabin. And if you ever travel in space, don't forget to keep your mouth closed while you are brushing your teeth! You can readily understand, then, the challenges that faced the space engineers when they had to design the Apollo spacecraft with all the mentioned, and other, requirements that had to be met.

America's first tottering steps toward a man in space were brought about by Project Mercury. In simple terms, the purpose of the Mercury program was to determine as far as possible what effects space would have on man. Would he be able to stand long periods of weightlessness without ill effects? And how would he react to the high forces experienced during the boost into orbit? Mercury, it turned out, consisted of only six manned launches, and only four of these put spacecraft into earth orbit. Two vehicles were used—the Redstone for the two suborbital launches and the Atlas for the four orbital launches.

Much was learned about the Mercury spacecraft, prior to its being manned, by a series of launch tests performed in the Little Joe series. These tests, at the NASA launch site at Wallops Island, Virginia, helped to prove out a design for the heat shield to protect the spacecraft during its fiery dash from space down through the earth's atmosphere. The Little Joe tests also evaluated the performance of a launch escape system to be used in case of an on-pad or early trajectory emergency.

One of the first to ride in the Mercury spacecraft was a thirty-seven pound "astrochimp" named Ham, who was rocketed to an altitude of 155 miles and downrange 420 miles. This flight demonstrated the ability of Ham to react normally and without ill effects under the conditions of weightlessness. Several other monkeys participated in the Mercury program. One of them, Enos, circled the globe twice.

The first manned Mercury launch occurred on May 5, 1961, when Astronaut Alan B. Shephard rode a Mercury spacecraft into space with a ballistic lob down the Eastern Test Range.

His 116-mile trip seems insignificant by today's standards, but it was the first flight of a well-thought-out plan which will eventually lead us to the moon. The Liberty Bell 7 spacecraft, piloted by Astronaut Virgil L. Grissom, was also launched on a similar ballistic trajectory, but premature loss of the escape hatch caused the spacecraft to take on water and sink.

Almost exactly three years after the Mercury contract had been won by the McDonnell Company, Astronaut John Glenn, boosted by an Atlas, was launched into a three-orbit mission that proved the flight-worthiness of the Mercury spacecraft. Three months later Astronaut Scott Carpenter also successfully completed a three-orbit mission in which several important experiments were carried out. This was followed by the six-orbit mission of Walter Schirra. The Mercury program was brought to a successful close with the twenty-two-orbit mission of Gordon Cooper, at the close of which a near perfect landing was made within sight of the main recovery ship. America's first man-in-space program had done well.

President Kennedy's 1961 announcement approving the moon try made it evident to the engineers that capabilities in addition to those developed in the Mercury program would be required to accomplish the Apollo mission. And it was from this reasoning that the Gemini program was born. Gemini is the name of a distant constellation of stars. Greek mythology tells us that the god Zeus, after the death of his twin son Castor, agreed to let the other twin, Pollux, share the heavens with his brother. Placed on the twin stars of Gemini, the brothers were charged with giving divine protection to distant voyagers. The Gemini program would build a firm foundation for the Apollo program.

The purpose of the Gemini program, the results of which

would be used directly in the upcoming Apollo program, was to investigate the extremely long flight, develop the technique of joining two vehicles in space and allow an astronaut to exit the spacecraft and maneuver in space.

NASA chose the Mercury contractor, the McDonnell Company, to build the two-man Gemini. Although the Gemini closely resembled the Mercury, there were several major differences. Along with holding two astronauts instead of the one in the Mercury, Gemini incorporated aircraft-like ejection seats for escape as opposed to the rocket escape system of the Mercury. Immediately aft of the Gemini spacecraft is an adapter section which remains attached until it is jettisoned at reentry. This adapter section contains storage tanks and other special equipment no longer needed by the time the mission-ending retro maneuver is begun.

The Gemini program, which lasted from April, 1964, to November, 1966, consisted of twelve very successful launches. The first two flight vehicles, Gemini I and II, were unmanned and were for the purpose of qualifying the Titan II launch vehicle and the heat shield. Following the three-orbit check-out flight of Gemini III, manned by astronauts Grissom and John Young, a truly remarkable feat was accomplished on Gemini IV when astronaut Ed White took America's first walk in space. Gemini orbited the earth 206 times, the longest flight to date. Major progress also was made in the launching of Gemini VI and VII within eleven days of each other and off the same pad. The two spacecraft actually flew in formation as they circled the earth.

The Gemini VIII mission demonstrated a technique that would later be required in the Apollo program—a rendezvous and docking with another spacecraft while in orbit.

he Titan II launch vehicle lifts off its pad at Cape Kennedy carrying a two-man
emini spacecraft.

The vehicle to which Gemini VIII was mated was an Agena stage that had previously been placed in orbit. The mission unfortunately had to be terminated early because of a malfunctioning thruster on the target vehicle. Gemini IX's basic mission objectives were not met because the docking target failed to drop its nose shroud.

Gemini X was a highly successful mission. It demonstrated the docking of the Gemini and the Agena and the using of the Agena's propulsion system while the two were joined. Astronaut Michael Collins actually left his Gemini spacecraft and retrieved experimental equipment aboard the Agena. Gemini XI had a much more ambitious mission, a rendezvous with the Agena target on the first orbit. Previous missions had required several orbits for this to take place. The Gemini program was brought to a close with the launching of the Gemini XII on November 11, 1966. The mission, ninety-four hours long, tested further many of the techniques that had been demonstrated on previous missions. It is now planned that the Gemini space capsule will be used as a part of the United States Air Force Manned Orbital Laboratory (MOL) program.

At the conclusion of the Gemini program, all eyes turned toward Apollo. Understandably, many of the principles that had been learned and tested in Mercury and Gemini had helped to shape the design of Apollo. The Apollo payload, like those of the long-duration Gemini missions, requires an adapter section to hold the necessary stores. Owing to the complexities of the Apollo profile, the payload consists of three modules—command, service and lunar. The entire Apollo spacecraft assembly weighs about 100,000 pounds and stands 82 feet high.

his high-angle view of the Saturn V shows particularly well the Apollo payload
ith its launch escape system.

The command module (CM), which rests at the very top of the Saturn V/Apollo combination, provides the working and living quarters for the three astronauts for the trip to the moon and return. Weighing about 6½ tons, the cone-shaped module is 13 feet in diameter and 11 feet high. The CM consists of both an inner and an outer shell, the inner being the crew compartment and the outer, a stainless honeycomb heatshield. The varied environments and stresses to be faced by the CM had to be carefully considered by the designers—the 5000-degree heat of reentry, the extreme cold of space, the load pressures and the launch and landing shocks.

Within the crew compartment of the CM is a hatch through which the astronauts can pass to the lunar module (LM), located directly to the rear. Four windows in the compartment provide the astronauts, while in flight, with a privileged view of the amazing space world. These windows also allow the astronauts to make certain navigational readings during the flight.

Within the crew compartment of the CM, the astronauts, lying on their backs in body-molded seats, face a maze of instrument panels. There are 550 switches and 71 lights for the astronauts to worry about. The communications, power and the other required subsystems are served by miles of wire. The CM provides 73 cubic feet of living space for each astronaut, an amount equal to that enjoyed by the passenger of a compact automobile.

Mounted directly atop the CM is the launch escape system, a latticework tower. The escape system is jettisoned after about 35 seconds into second stage burn.

Directly beneath the CM is a space 2 feet high and 13 feet long leading to the service module (SM). The SM houses

The Apollo command module is lifted into position for mating with the service module, which is located directly beneath.

many of the subsystems to support the crew within the CM. The SM, 13 feet in diameter and 22 feet long, also contains the main propulsion system for the Apollo payload. Generating a thrust of almost 23 tons, the SM single-engine propulsion system will be used several times during the lunar trip. It will apply braking so that the spacecraft can be inserted into a lunar orbit, and will make midcourse corrections on the trip to the moon and return. This extra propulsion system was made necessary because the S-IVB third stage will have been jettisoned after it has given the spacecraft the speed to escape out of the earth parking orbit. After performing all its prescribed functions, the SM is jettisoned before the CM's reentry back through the earth's atmosphere.

Underneath the SM is an adapter section connecting the module to the top of the S-IVB third stage. The adapter section is conical in shape so that it will be able to match the 13-foot diameter of the SM and the 22-foot diameter of the S-IVB stage. The most important function of this adapter, however, is the housing of the lunar module (LM), in which two of the three astronauts will go to the moon and return from lunar orbit. The LM adapter, composed of four sections, is opened up with the small explosive charges, thus allowing the LM to be turned loose and mated with the front of the CM.

Resembling an insect, the LM is designed to carry two of the Apollo astronauts to the surface of the moon, sustain them while they are there, and then provide them the propulsive means to rendezvous with the CM in lunar orbit. The LM consists of two distinct parts that enable it to accomplish its critical job—the descent and the ascent stages.

The descent stage, which will be used to land the LM on the lunar surface, has an eight-sided shape about 10 feet in height. Constructed of aluminum alloy, the descent stage has its own propulsion system for lowering the LM for a soft landing. Its rocket engine, mounted on a gimbal, can provide from 1000 to almost 11,000 pounds of thrust. The descent stage will first touch the lunar surface on its landing gear, which consists of four legs mounted on outriggers. An aluminum disk is mounted on the end of each leg to assure a stable footing. The descent stage will be used only for the lunar landing phase, and will be left on the moon. It will, however, serve as the launch pad for the ascent stage, which is mounted directly above it.

The ascent stage contains the crew compartment, a fixed-position propulsion system with 3500 pounds of thrust, and the necessary instruments to control the stage during its ascent to the lunar orbit. Once again, as was true with the other components of the Saturn V/Apollo combination, the ascent stage is discarded after it has fulfilled its mission. After it has docked with the CM in lunar orbit and the crew has been transferred, the ascent stage is abandoned in the lunar orbit.

There are, of course, elaborate communication links between all portions of the Apollo payload. It is possible for the astronaut remaining in the circling CM to remain in contact with the two on the lunar surface, and it is also possible for an astronaut inside the LM to remain in contact with the one outside the LM. A series of small reaction motors on both the command and the service modules provide the small thrusts required to make small velocity changes and perform spacecraft stabilization functions. The navigation system for the Apollo payload includes both an inertial system and a flight computer. Also available to the astronauts is a sextant, which will enable them to sight on the moon and stars in order to check their position before a maneuver is initiated.

Fuel cells in the SM convert a mixture of hydrogen and oxygen directly into electricity for the operation of the on-board systems. Manufacturing water for the crew and for cooling the equipment are also functions of these cells. Three batteries aboard the CM will provide the power after the SM has been jettisoned.

The Apollo spacecraft was designed to accomplish one and one mission only—to go to the moon. But, undoubtedly, in the years to come the Apollo hardware or close models of it will be used in even more ambitious manned space flights—maybe even for a trip to Mars!

12

Timetable
to the Moon

Once you have acquired the necessary hardware to go to the moon, you can not just suit up your astronauts and send them speeding away on the first launch. There needs to be a carefully thought-out schedule which will assure the best chance of success when the day for the lunar mission arrives. Of course, this schedule cannot be fixed far in advance, since many unknown difficulties could arise in either the Saturn V or the Apollo payload that could cause the timetable to be delayed. Some problems could cause postponements for many months, while others might not be serious enough to cause any delay at all.

In the case of the Apollo program, there is a schedule for both the Saturn V launch vehicle and the Apollo payload. With the Saturn V, it is necessary to assure that the vehicle is made as safe as possible for astronauts, a technique aptly known as "man-rating." With a new vehicle like the Saturn V, man-rating must be a very careful process, as the flight characteristics of the vehicle are not known. In the Mercury and Gemini programs, the use of tested vehicles—Redstone, Atlas and Titan—aided in the man-rating process. NASA decided that two unmanned launches would be required to man-rate the Saturn V vehicle. These two launches have already occurred in the form of the Apollo 4 and Apollo 6 missions. The Apollo 7 manned launch was carried out during the last part of 1968. The two man-rating flights proved that the Saturn V vehicle was sound, and should be able to accomplish the trip to earth orbit easily. The second man-rating flight, however, was not completely successful, a fact that prompted speculation that another unmanned flight might be required before the Saturn V could be man-rated.

The Apollo 4 mission, explained in detail in Chapter I, was one of the greatest, if not the greatest, launch attempts ever to take place at Cape Kennedy. No one in his wildest dreams ever imagined that this massive beast with its thousands of untried components would function so perfectly the first time. This launch brought great hopes from all concerned in the program that the huge technological problems standing in the way of a successful lunar landing were rapidly being closed. All three stages of the vehicle, performing as planned, placed the Saturn V on the exact trajectory. No structural or vibration problems were encountered during the flight. Up until this time, NASA had anticipated the need for three unmanned flights, but the tremendous Apollo 4 success prompted thinking toward eliminating the third unmanned flight.

The second Saturn V launch unfortunately did not meet with the success of the first. As the Apollo 6 vehicle lifted off its pad on April 4, 1968, the ground controllers had visions of a repeat performance of the Apollo 4 mission. Their expectations, however, were not realized, since after only six minutes into the flight, the Saturn V suffered the first of a number of setbacks. Two of the five J-2 engines of the S-II stage prematurely shut down. The crisis was not fatal, however, as the remaining three engines continued to burn longer than programed owing to the extra propellant which the two shutdown engines had not consumed.

But there were still more problems ahead for the Apollo 6 mission. Since the premature shutdown caused the S-II stage to be slower at burnout than programed, the guidance computer commanded the S-IVB stage to burn about 30 seconds longer to make up the difference. This additional burn-time depleted ten tons of additional S-IVB propellant, fuel that was to have been used when the S-IVB was restarted after a two-orbit coast. Aimed at a 115-mile circular orbit, the Apollo 6 payload was finally placed into a 110- by 225-mile elliptical orbit. If the Apollo 6 had been carrying men for the lunar trip, the mission would probably have been aborted. Since the purpose of this flight was to have the Saturn V place a payload into orbit, the mission was in effect a success even though it was in the wrong orbit.

One more difficulty, however, was to lie ahead in this hard-luck mission. Following a two-orbit coast, the S-IVB stage failed to reignite when commanded from the ground to do so. The purpose of this second S-IVB burn was to propel the payload to a distance of 322,000 miles into space. This maneuver would be quite similar to that which S-IVB would be required to perform in the actual lunar mission.

To salvage what they could from the Apollo 6 mission, the NASA ground controllers commanded the 21,500-pound-thrust service module engine to drive the spacecraft to a 13,821-mile altitude, which was far short of the planned 322,-000-mile apogee. Later analysis of the flight revealed that the early shutdown of the two J-2 engines was due to the improper installation of two wires. A leak in one of the propellant lines probably was responsible for the failure of the S-IVB to reignite in orbit. It was not the Saturn V that failed, but the men who served her.

153

The Apollo spacecraft has been under hardware test for a somewhat longer time than the Saturn V launch vehicle. Actually, the first early versions of the Apollo were boosted into orbit by the sixth and seventh Saturn I launches in 1964. These early boilerplate models provided useful information in determining the final design of the spacecraft. The Apollo's test schedule was continued by the Saturn IB launch vehicle, starting with the suborbital launch of an early version of the spacecraft in 1966. This launch tested the propulsion system of the service module and the heat shield of the command module. Late in 1968 the Saturn IB 205 mission boosted three astronauts into orbit in order to check out the command and the service modules.

The 205 mission, which was better known as Apollo 7, helped provide great confidence in the operation of the command and service modules. Astronauts Schirra, Eisele and Cunningham spent almost eleven days in orbit. This mission included such unique experiments as live television transmissions of the crew and rendezvousing with the spent S-IVB stage. The flight proved that the command and service modules were indeed ready for the lunar trip.

The Saturn V and the Apollo were brought together for the first time in the previously discussed Apollo 4 mission. Although Apollo 4's basic mission was to prove the Saturn V, a secondary goal was reached when the command module survived launch, space flight and reentry without structural damage. The heatshield withstood the reentry heating without crumbling or flaking away. The Apollo 6 mission also provided some information on the flight-worthiness of the spacecraft— although not as much as had been hoped for, since the planned reentry velocity was not reached.

Courtesy NASA

Recovery of the unmanned Apollo command module at the conclusion of the Apollo 6 mission launched from Kennedy Space Center on April 4, 1968.

The Apollo spacecraft check-out program suffered a sad setback on January 27, 1967, when Astronauts Grissom, White and Roger Chaffee died in a disastrous fire at Launch Complex 34. The fire, occurring within the command module atop Saturn IB, brought great grief to the nation, which had lost three young spacemen whose greatest dream was to go to the moon. It is to these three brave men that this book is dedicated.

The Apollo program was shaken to its very roots by the fire, and many suggestions were immediately submitted to try to prevent such an event from ever happening again. Many changes have been made in the Apollo spacecraft since that fateful day, among which is the almost complete removal of the flammable materials which contributed substantially to the fire. A quick exit escape hatch has also been incorporated in the command module.

The complete Apollo spacecraft will now be atop the Saturn V for all the remaining launches leading to the final lunar landing. This mating will start with the upcoming 503 mission, probably to take place in late 1968. This trip will check out the operations of the command and service modules within earth orbit. There will also be docking experiments and extravehicular activity.

This first manned Saturn V launch will be followed by the more ambitious 504 mission. This undertaking envisions a ten- to fourteen-day in-orbit check-out, including an excursion out to 4000 miles to simulate a transfer to the moon. The following 505 mission will probably have a mission profile very similar to that of 504.

It is very hard to predict exactly what the lunar landing program will be from this point on. NASA may decide, owing to some problem with either the Saturn V or the Apollo, that one or more additional flights are required. Or things may proceed at such a favorable pace that some of the proving flights can be eliminated. Only time will tell.

The lunar landing will probably be accomplished on the eighth or ninth Saturn V launch. Very recently, the decision was made by NASA to include a circumlunar flight as a prerequisite to the actual landing. A successful completion of the circumlunar mission would probably result in a lunar landing attempt on the next mission.

With the modification of the Apollo spacecraft following the 1967 fire catastrophe and the knowledge gained from the flight tests of the Saturn V in the Apollo 4 and 6 missions, the Apollo program appears to be well on its way to a lunar landing in late 1969 or 1970.

13

The Mission
to the Moon

The Saturn V launch vehicle and its Apollo payload work together to perform the lunar mission, and the method chosen, as mentioned earlier, is the lunar orbit rendezvous (LOR) technique. Of course, it was necessary to define the mission before the exact configuration and size of the launch vehicle and the payload could be fixed. Several methods of reaching the moon were considered before the LOR technique was decided on. Two others that were considered seriously were the direct injection method and the earth orbit rendezvous (EOR) method.

The direct injection method uses one launch vehicle to accomplish the mission. The term "direct" aptly describes this mission technique, as the vehicle is launched directly to the moon without stopping in an earth parking orbit. There is also no lunar parking orbit, as in the LOR technique.

The earth orbit rendezvous technique envisioned sending into a low earth parking orbit two separate launch vehicles, each to carry a part of the lunar spacecraft as its payload. The second vehicle would be launched and placed in the orbit and vicinity of the first vehicle. The two vehicles would then rendezvous and physically join. Once the spacecraft had been assembled in orbit, it would be sent on its way for a direct landing on the moon. The spacecraft would be required to provide the complete propulsive power for the trip back to earth.

EOR would also require four identical launch pads—two for the mission and two for a backup. This could have been one of the major reasons for discarding the EOR technique.

So, after careful study, the LOR technique was selected to perform the lunar mission. This method considerably reduced the propulsive power required for landing and taking off from the moon. This reduction in propulsion in the LOR was possible because it is only necessary for the spacecraft to rendezvous with the moon-orbiting remainder of the rocket, which would provide the propulsion for the rest of the return trip. NASA felt in 1962, when the LOR decision was made, that possibly up to two years would thus be shaved off the Apollo timetable, along with a cost saving of 10 to 15 percent over each of the other two methods. Also, when the LOR decision was made, NASA was considering the possibility of launching an unmanned lunar logistics vehicle that would be prepositioned on the moon before the actual manned launch. This vehicle would provide the astronauts with oxygen, instrumentation and other equipment which otherwise would have to be carried in the manned Apollo spacecraft. It was later decided, however, that the logistics vehicle would not be required, and the idea was dropped.

Since 1962 the Apollo mission profile has had many changes made in it, but the same basic mission plan has been retained. Let's imagine that it is launch day sometime in 1969 or 1970. This is the way it will be at that exciting time.

The initial ascent trajectory uses the first two stages and a portion of the third stage in order to achieve the necessary 25,600-feet-per-second velocity for the 100 nautical mile parking orbit. The S-IC first stage burns for approximately 160 seconds after lifting off the pad, and burns out at an altitude of about 36 miles. During this first-stage burn period the S-IC stage acquires a burnout velocity of 7600 feet per second, or about one fourth of that required to make orbit.

Following a short coast period, during which the first stage is jettisoned, the S-II second stage ignites and burns for the extremely long time of almost 400 seconds. Shortly after S-II ignition, the launch escape system is jettisoned, since it will no longer be needed and carrying it along would lower the overall performance of the launch vehicle. S-II stage burnout occurs at an altitude of about 500,000 feet at a speed of about 21,000 feet per second.

The S-IVB third stage will be ignited shortly after S-II burnout and jettison. As the S-II stage does not achieve orbital velocity, it will reenter the earth's atmosphere. But the stage will break up and burn to a cinder before it hits the water. The 200,000-pound thrust of the S-IVB third stage will then drive the Apollo spacecraft into the parking orbit. It will accomplish the orbit insertion by burning about 160 seconds, with the actual orbit insertion occurring about 1400 miles downrange. We are now about twelve minutes into the mission.

Once the S-IVB has shut down in orbit, it will coast for less than an orbit with the Apollo payload firmly attached to its forward end. Since the launch escape system was jettisoned earlier, the lunar module docking mechanism is now exposed on top of the CM. A slight force produced by venting propellant is exerted on the vehicle in order to stabilize the high-energy propellants within the S-IVB stage. The inertial guidance system contained within the instrument unit provides the attitude control for the S-IVB and Apollo payload while it is in its orbital coast mode. A set of small rocket motors located on the S-IVB stage takes the commands generated within the instrument unit and converts them into the required thrust to stabilize the vehicle.

After this orbital coast phase, during which a complete check-out of men and equipment is performed, it is time to enter the next phase of the lunar trip. At a prearranged time, the S-IVB stage is reignited for a burn period of about 310 seconds, during which the S-IVB stage will add about 10,600 feet per second to the spacecraft's speed. This escape velocity is that which is required to overcome the force of the earth's gravity. Once the S-IVB has been shut down from its second burn, the job of the Saturn V is done. From this point on until the end of the mission, all propulsive forces will be provided by the spacecraft. Once the escape velocity maneuver has been accomplished, the spacecraft and third stage will coast together through space for about an hour. Normally the guidance system within the instrument unit will not require any update; but if there should be a change in the basic position profile, this information would be transmitted to the instrument unit from ground-based transmitters of the MSFN. If, however, there should be a failure of the instrument computer during the lunar injection burn, a computer aboard the CM would enable the spacecraft to complete the mission.

About twenty minutes into the mission, the next portion of the flight is scheduled to take place—transposition and docking. This complicated maneuver, one of the most important in the Apollo mission profile, is begun by opening the adapter section between the SM and the S-IVB stage. Small explosive charges swing apart the four sections of the adapter like peeling a banana. At this time, the SM/CM combination breaks away, and turns completely around so that the front of the CM is facing the top of the LM. The CM will then insert its docking mechanism onto the LM, and pull the LM away from the burned-out S-IVB and adapter. All of these maneuvers are occurring at a velocity of 36,500 feet per second; but since there is no atmosphere, this can be accomplished easily.

As the spacecraft coasts farther and farther away from the earth, its velocity is gradually slowed. This decrease in speed results because the earth's gravity continues to affect the spacecraft out to a distance of about 200,000 miles, or about 80 percent of the way to the moon. At this point the gravity of the moon becomes the greater force acting on the spacecraft, and the velocity understandably begins to increase. When the spacecraft arrives in the vicinity of the moon, its speed will have been reduced from 36,500 to about 8500 feet per second. However, since the velocity required for the 80-mile-high lunar orbit is considerably less than 8500 feet per second, it will be necessary to slow the spacecraft in order to accomplish the injection into lunar orbit. This decrease in speed is accomplished by the SM's propulsion system, which, pointed toward the moon, is fired for almost seven minutes in order to slow the spacecraft. Once the spacecraft has been put into orbit at an altitude of 80 miles above the moon's surface, it will take about two hours for it to make one complete orbit.

After circling the moon twice, during which time all the equipment will be carefully checked again, two of the three astronauts will transfer to the lunar module, which is attached to the front of the CM. The method of entry into the LM is through the docking hatch located on the front of the CM. After the transfer has been accomplished, small reaction motors on the LM will push it away from the lone-astronaut-manned CM. The two portions of the Apollo payload will then coast together until the LM has reached the exact location at which to begin its trip to the lunar surface. Of course, for the LM to land on the surface, it will be necessary to adjust its speed to slower than orbital velocity. When the speed is reduced only 100 feet per second, the LM goes into a long ballistic glide that carries it halfway around the moon. As the lunar surface is approached, the descent engine will be ignited again, an action that allows the astronauts to maneuver the LM in a way quite similar to that of a helicopter and finally to place it softly on the lunar surface. The astronaut remaining in the CM will continue to orbit the moon during the time the other two astronauts are exploring the lunar surface.

Many of the unmanned NASA lunar probes have been concerned with finding the best possible landing site for the LM. The chosen site will need to be relatively free of boulders and away from large ridges that might wreck the LM at touchdown. At the time this book is being written, NASA had narrowed the number of possible landing sites to five. All of them are located near the equator, a condition that is very important, since sites not close to the equator would require more fuel for the landing. These equator sites also provide the best light from the sun, another condition that will aid in the landing operation.

Once on the moon, the two astronauts will probably leave the LM together during each of the two times they will venture out onto the lunar surface. When they do set foot on the moon for the first time, some will call this event the greatest accomplishment of man. Historians in the centuries to come will look on this landing as an event even greater than Columbus' discovery of America. Still, probably ten years after the event, this first landing may seem insignificant to many, as the first manned orbital Mercury flight of John Glenn now seems when it is compared to Apollo. The great accomplishments of bygone days are quickly forgotten by almost everyone except the historians. But it should be remembered that the Wright brothers, Charles Lindbergh and John Glenn showed the way for the progress that was to come.

Among the many experiments planned while the astronauts are on the lunar surface is the attempt to send live television back to earth. Packages also will be left on the surface of the moon to transmit information back to earth for many months. After the second trip out of the LM, it will be time to start planning for the journey back to the CM, which will still be revolving in its orbit. The ascent trajectory, a delicate maneuver, is initiated when the CM is slightly ahead of the LM. Only the ascent stage of the LM leaves the lunar surface; the descent stage, having served its purpose, is abandoned.

The force for the first step of the return trip is provided by the ascent-stage propulsion system, which powers the stage on a flat trajectory covering about 160 miles on the surface while rising only about 10 miles. The hookup with the CM will be accomplished by the small thrusters on both the LM and the CM. Once the docking has been completed, the two astronauts within the LM ascent stage will transfer back into the CM to receive a warm welcome from the other astronaut. The ascent stage is then detached from the CM and left in lunar orbit. Then preparations will begin for the long trip back to earth— one quarter of a million miles away!

After still another equipment checkout, the SM is started for what will be a two-minute burn period to drive the spacecraft out of the lunar orbit and toward the soft green hills of earth. The SM will also make several midcourse corrections on the return trip, as it did on the outgoing journey. The trip

MISSION PROFILE

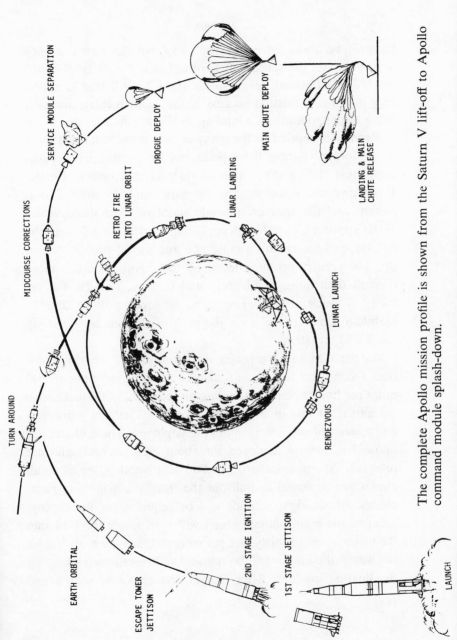

SERVICE MODULE SEPARATION

DROGUE DEPLOY

MAIN CHUTE DEPLOY

LANDING & MAIN CHUTE RELEASE

MIDCOURSE CORRECTIONS

RETRO FIRE INTO LUNAR ORBIT

LUNAR LANDING

TURN AROUND

LUNAR LAUNCH

RENDEZVOUS

EARTH ORBITAL

ESCAPE TOWER JETTISON

2ND STAGE IGNITION

1ST STAGE JETTISON

LAUNCH

The complete Apollo mission profile is shown from the Saturn V lift-off to Apollo command module splash-down.

time will be about three days each way, but this time can vary somewhat. As the spacecraft approaches the vicinity of earth, the SM is jettisoned, leaving only the CM. All that is necessary now for a mission success is the earth reentry that will bring the astronauts to a landing in the Pacific Ocean.

Reentry is another of the many critical maneuvers that must be performed during the Apollo mission profile. The spacecraft must "hit" a thirty-mile corridor at the correct altitude. If the approach is too shallow, the earth could be missed completely, and the spacecraft would shoot off into space again. If the approach were too steep, the spacecraft would meet the full force of the earth's atmosphere and would probably burn up. The reentry problem faced by the Apollo is much more difficult than those of Mercury and Gemini, because the velocity is much greater. The crew, however, will be able to maintain some control over the path of the reentry by using small CM thrusters.

As the CM races through the atmosphere, the drag produced slows the vehicle so that it is traveling only about 200 miles per hour when it reaches an altitude of 25,000 feet above the earth. At this time the protective heatshield is jettisoned, and a series of small parachutes are deployed. These chutes are allowed to remain deployed for about eight seconds and are released. At an altitude of 10,000 feet another set of small chutes are deployed to pull out the three main landing parachutes. About eight seconds will be required for the deployment of the main chutes, which will then lower the CM into the water at about thirty feet per second. Once the craft has hit the water, the chutes will be released to prevent their dragging the floating module. After impact, the elaborate search and recovery force will locate the module, pluck it from the water and place it on the deck of the main recovery ship.

The celebrations will have to wait, for as soon as they are recovered the astronauts will be under strict quarantine. The reason for this quarantine is that there is a possibility that alien organisms could hitch a ride in the spacecraft, in the astronauts' bodies, or in the soil samples that will be brought back. Such organisms, against which man probably would have no immunity, could cause an epidemic on earth. So it is necessary that every precaution be taken. If all goes well, however, and there are no "lunar bugs," the returning heroes will receive their belated and quite deserving heroes' welcome.

14

The Many Faces of Saturn V

In these days when NASA is finding it more and more difficult to get money to continue the United States space effort, the likelihood of seeing a new launch vehicle in the near future appears quite unlikely. The tremendous amount of money required to develop a new launch system is just not available. A much more economic approach would be to modify existing launch vehicles so that they will be able to satisfy the new payload requirements. The two techniques that can be used are to either decrease or increase the performance of existing launch vehicles, quite expectably being called derating and uprating. In some cases using only a portion of an existing launcher could produce the desired results.

There appears to be a real payload gap between the Saturn IB and the Saturn V. Some of the methods considered for uprating the Saturn IB to fill the gap were strapping on solid-fueled boosters and adding propellant additives to the first stage. Although the Saturn IB could, with extensive uprating, have a payload approaching 100,000 pounds in orbit, modifications to the Saturn V could also produce a vehicle with that capability. Several intermediate Saturn V vehicles have been studied, providing a payload capability of from 50,000 to 180,000 pounds in earth orbit. The savings that could be realized in developing these vehicles using proven Saturn V hardware would be significant. Another advantage of this concept is that all existing design, fabrication, transportation and launch facilities could continue to be utilized, thus eliminating the necessity for construction of new facilities.

The first logical modification in derating the performance of the Saturn V, and the one requiring fewest changes, would be to eliminate the S-II stage. The Saturn V would then consist of a S-IC/S-IVB configuration. Since, under the modification, the 7,500,000-pound thrust of the S-IC would be much too high for the lightened vehicle, it would be necessary to eliminate the center F-1 engine in order to bring the lift-off thrust-to-weight ratio back into reasonable bounds. A payload of about 130,000 pounds, or about three times that of the Saturn IB, could be expected from this vehicle. This inexpensive configuration could be ready to fly twelve months after the official go-ahead was given.

A promising concept is that in which a modified S-IC stage is fired into orbit by itself. In this situation, certain changes to the standard S-IC configuration would be required, as the 160-second burn-time from the five F-1 engines would be far too short to allow the payload to be inserted into orbit. The scheme being considered uses a stage-and-a-half concept similar to that of the Atlas ICBM. Lifting off in the normal manner, four F-1 engines would be jettisoned at the time when 70 percent of its fuel had been consumed. The center F-1 engine, continuing to burn, would finally inject the payload into orbit.

Another interesting intermediate vehicle concept also envisions using portions of the Saturn V—but not the parts you might expect. Reference here is to the S-II ground start vehicle, which eliminates entirely the S-IC first stage, with the normal S-II second stage now becoming the first stage. This vehicle would use the same Launch Complex 39 pads, with an extra structure supporting the vehicle and replacing the space normally occupied by the S-IC stage. This arrangement would also enable the S-II/S-IVB to utilize the same service arms that it would use in its normal Saturn V configuration. However, owing to the low thrust produced by the S-II stage, which was designed as an altitude stage, the orbital payload would be quite low, about 20,000 pounds.

But this payload can be greatly increased if the vehicle is helped along during the early portions of its flight trajectory. This helping force could come from solid-fueled strap-on rocket motors mounted to the sides of the S-II first stage. Payloads of more than 100,000 pounds can be realized when 120-inch solids are used either in conjunction with the S-II stage or by burning as a zero stage, with the S-II stage igniting at the altitude following solid booster burnout.

It follows then that a very flexible stable of intermediate launch vehicles could be established by using various parts of the Saturn V. Developing one or all of these vehicles could be brought about rather inexpensively, since much of the basic testing work on Saturn V has already been done.

What comes after Saturn V? The original NASA plans called for the establishment of a Saturn V follow-on booster, called the Nova, which would completely dwarf the Saturn V.

It now appears that if a greater capability in both size and capability than that of the Saturn V is to be developed, it will come as an improved model of the Saturn V. One of the major factors when considering uprating the Saturn V is that the new vehicle be able to use the present Cape Kennedy facilities. That is, the new vehicle should be able to be assembled in the Vehicle Assembly Building and fit onto the mobile launchers. Many of the same improvement techniques for the Saturn IB

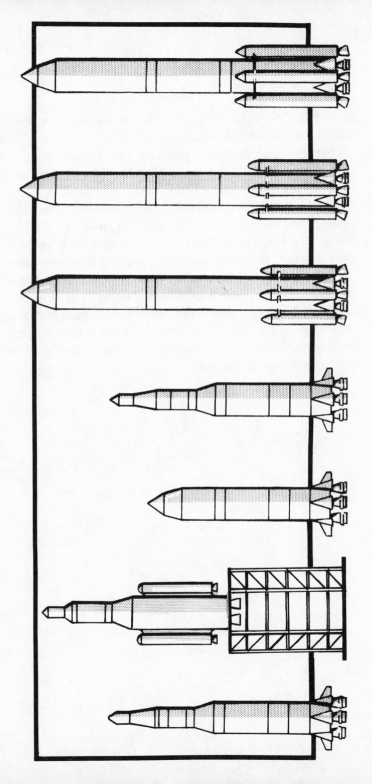

The four vehicles on the left are intermediate versions of the Saturn V providing payloads up to about 200,000 pounds. The three uprated Saturn V vehicles on the right incorporate solid motors with diameters of 120, 156 and 260 inches.

have already received considerable attention in preliminary thinking about an uprated Saturn V.

One of these uprating plans is the technique of using solid strap-ons with diameters of 120, 156 or 260 inches. Payloads up to three times that currently attainable are possible by using various combinations of these solid motors. Other payload improvements are possible by using a 1,800,000-pound thrust version of the F-1 along with stretching the S-IC stage in order to accommodate a greater propellant capacity.

Over the long run the Saturn V may prove to be much more important to the overall United Space effort than in its current role as the moon rocket. And when one considers the great payload potential that can be acquired from Saturn V uprating, the United States space requirements can probably be satisfied for many years to come.

15 The Future

Although we haven't yet made the trip, the United States has a powerful new launch vehicle and a highly sophisticated spacecraft capable of taking men to the moon and back. This complicated combination was specifically designed from the very start to perform the manned lunar mission, but plans are under way even now for other uses of the Saturn V and its Apollo payload.

The immediate plans of NASA beyond the Apollo programs are in the form of the Apollo Applications Program (AAP), which will consist of eighteen launches. By current planning, the AAP will officially get under way in 1970 and extend until 1973 or 1974. The program will utilize both the Saturn IB and the Saturn V as launch vehicles, with the first parts of AAP dealing with ambitious experiments in earth orbit. One of the first major efforts will be the establishment of an orbital workshop built from a burned-out S-IVB stage of a Saturn IB. The workshop would be docked to an Apollo spacecraft, with an airlock connecting the two vehicles. Missions of this type would vary from fourteen to fifty-six days in orbit. Another major part of the experiments would be viewing of the universe with a telescope in earth orbit. These pictures would provide man with a much better view than he has ever had, as he wouldn't have to look through the dense layers of the earth's atmosphere.

AAP earth orbital missions in 1973 will attempt to maintain a space station in orbit for a whole year. The station would be placed into orbit by a two-stage Saturn V, with the station situated in that part of the rocket formerly occupied by the third stage. The station would be supplied four times during the year by the Saturn IB's, and it would remain manned by at least one astronaut at all times. The advantage of such a long orbital life program is that extensive experiments could be undertaken, such as examining the effects of weightlessness on the astronaut for long periods of time. Preliminary work on the program is expected to begin in 1970.

The last part of the AAP has as its main purpose the exploration of the moon started by the initial Apollo lunar landing. As currently planned, the exploration would be carried out with four Saturn V launches—one each for the first two missions and two for the final mission. The first two missions will have a stay time of three days on the moon. It is estimated that the lifetime of the lunar module can be increased in order to allow the three-day stay time. A small flying vehicle will be carried on the lunar module in order to allow one astronaut to cover more surface while exploring the moon.

The first long-duration lunar AAP launch will probably not take place until the mid-1970's, when a dual launch of Saturn V's would occur. The first Saturn V would place on the lunar surface an LM without the ascent stage. Into the space of the ascent stage would go the necessary life-support equipment to sustain the astronauts for a seven- to fourteen-day mission. The second Saturn V would launch the normal Apollo payload to the lunar surface in the vicinity of the first payload. As was true in the Apollo mission, one astronaut would remain in the CM/SM combination in lunar orbit while the other two go to the lunar surface.

Another future concept using Saturn V hardware involves assembling the necessary elements in orbit to accomplish a manned flyby of Mars or Venus. This interesting technique employs a dual Saturn V launch, with rendezvous and docking occurring in earth orbit. The first Saturn V vehicle would launch the orbital escape stage to provide the velocity necessary to place the payload on its way to either Mars or Venus. We would have in effect a Saturn V with two S-II stages, one to be used during the boost to orbit and the upper S-II for the orbital escape. The second launch will place the payload into the same earth orbit, where it would rendezvous with the S-II escape stage, which will be in orbit. Specially designed "tankers" will then provide the stage with its oxidizer.

The S-II stage would be used in the escape applications of the planned mission because the S-IVB, designed for use with the Apollo, could not supply the greater velocity requirements. The large escape payload weight provided by the S-II would allow for the extra life-support equipment that would be required for the long travel times.

Considered also has been the addition to the Saturn V of a fourth stage, which could reduce the time to reach the planets. The Atlas Centaur stage, propelled by high-energy fuel, is a possibility for this application. A three-stage Saturn V could boost a 24,000-pound payload to Jupiter in 750 days, while the four-stage vehicle would reduce this time to about 500 days. This shortened trip time is quite important when one considers the aging effect of the on-board instruments that must operate when the vicinity of the planet is reached.

The Saturn V could also be used in unmanned missions,

which could add materially to our knowledge of the origin of the universe. One of these missions would be the probing and sampling of a comet. Comets consist of a small solid nucleus several miles in diameter surrounded by a gaseous substance up to 5000 miles in diameter. A gaseous region called the tail trails the comet through space, sometimes stretching out millions of miles behind. Experiments that could be conducted when the comet was penetrated could determine the physical properties of the structure of the comet and the mass distribution as a function of the distance from the nucleus.

Another possible mission of great importance would be a solar probe to the sun. Radiation across the entire trip could thus be measured much better than is possible now from earth. The trip also would allow measurement of solar flares emitted by the sun. Total mission velocities of 43,000 to 53,000 feet per second would be required for this mission, with resulting four-stage Saturn V payloads of 5000 to 14,000 pounds.

The earth/moon libration points are two locations in which a satellite could remain in stable motion about the earth. Placing a satellite in these spots would allow information to be acquired on the gravitational fields surrounding the earth and moon. A satellite placed into this location would probably provide more information on the origin of the earth and moon than any other type of probe into space. The Saturn V would be able to place only about 76,000 pounds in this location in space as compared to the 100,000 pounds it can place into a lunar escape velocity. Using a fourth stage could increase this value to about 85,000 pounds.

If we want to consider flights, say, twenty years from now, we could think of exploration outside of our own solar system.

Such voyages would require a velocity of more than 55,000 feet per second. In order to obtain the extremely high velocities required by such a mission, there would have to be a great reduction in payload, possibly down to about 1000 pounds. But the really restricting phase of any out-of-the-solar-system flights is the tremendously long trip-times required. With the 1000-pound payload, it would take more than seven years for the Saturn V to boost a payload beyond the orbit of the planet Pluto.

Many of the previous discussions have mentioned the performance advantages that can be acquired in interplanetary missions by the addition of a fourth stage to the Saturn V. It is possible, too, in the 1970's that this fourth stage, or maybe even the third stage, might be nuclear-powered. The low-thrust, long-burn-time characteristics of the nuclear stage would make it highly desirable for the high-velocity interplanetary missions.

Through the use of a nuclear orbit escape stage, earth orbit weight on interplanetary flyby missions could be reduced about 30 percent. This reduction in weight could lead to considerable cost savings through fewer launches in the cases where earth orbital assembly was to be accomplished.

So the many faces of Saturn V will fulfill the space payload needs of the United States for many years to come, whether it be in its current Apollo form, augmented by large solid motors or topped with multiple upper stages, perhaps even a nuclear stage. Through the use of the Saturn V over a broad range of missions, the vast investment in the Apollo program will pay rich dividends in world prestige and leadership. Saturn V has a great future in space—and it is only beginning.

Appendix A

Saturn I Launches

Event	Date	Launch Site	Apogee (NM)	Perigee (NM)	Orbital Lifetime (Days)
SA-1	October 27, 1961	34	—	—	—
SA-2	April 25, 1962	34	—	—	—
SA-3	November 16, 1962	34	—	—	—
SA-4	March 28, 1963	34			
SA-5	January 29, 1964	37	416.5	141.6	823
SA-6	May 28, 1964	37	129.4	98.9	3.3
SA-7	September 18, 1964	37	126.4	97.3	3.8
SA-8	May 25, 1965	37	404.2	273.5	1220*
SA-9	February 16, 1965	37	402.3	268.1	1188*
SA-10	July 30, 1965	37	287.2	285.6	720*

* Predicted value

Appendix B

Saturn IB Launches

Event	Date	Launch Site	Apogee (NM)	Perigee (NM)	Mission
201	February 26, 1966	34	—	—	Ballistic
203	July 5, 1966	37	132	114	Orbital
202	August 25, 1966	34	—	—	Suborbital
204	January 22, 1968	37	120	85	Orbital
205	October 11, 1968	34	262	105	Orbital

Appendix C

Saturn V Launches

Apollo Mission	Launch Vehicle	Date	Launch Site	Perigee (NM)	Apogee (NM)	Mission Objective
4	501	November 9, 1967	39	99	103	Launch vehicle test
6	502	April 4, 1968	39	93	194	Launch vehicle test

Anticipated Future Launches in Support of the Apollo Program

	503	The 503 mission will emphasize operations with the complete Apollo spacecraft. The command module will carry the first crew to orbit.
	504	The 504 mission will carry the second three-man crew to orbit when the complete Apollo spacecraft will be exercised for lunar mission development.
	505	The 505 mission will probably be quite similar to 504.
	506	The 506 mission will have as its most optimistic goal to orbit the moon. If all would go well, a lunar landing could be attempted on this mission, but this is highly unlikely.
	507-509	It is impossible to predict on which mission the actual lunar landing will be accomplished. The NASA schedule is open ended and the maximum will be accomplished from each mission before proceeding to the next.

Appendix D

Mercury Flight Summary

Mission No. & Sequence	Type Mission	Date	Astronauts	Perigee and Apogee	Mission Duration
MA-1	Ballistic	July 29, 1960	—	—	—
MR-1	Ballistic	November 21, 1960	—	—	—
	Engine shutdown at launch				
MR-1A	Ballistic	December 19, 1960	—	—	—
MR-2	Ballistic	January 31, 1961	"Ham"*	—	—
MA-2	Ballistic	February 21, 1961	—	—	—
MA-3	Orbital attempt (failure)	April 25, 1961	Mechanical man	—	—
MR-3	Ballistic	May 5, 1961	A. Shephard	—	—
MR-4	Ballistic	July 21, 1961	V. Grissom	—	—
MA-4	Orbital	September 13, 1961	Mechanical man	100 NM and 159 NM	1 orbit
MA-5	Orbital	November 29, 1961	"Enos"*	99 NM and 146 NM	2 orbits
MA-6	Orbital	February 20, 1962	J. Glenn	98 NM and 159 NM	3 orbits
MA-7	Orbital	May 24, 1962	S. Carpenter	100 NM and 167 NM	3 orbits
MA-8	Orbital	October 3, 1962	W. Schirra	100 NM and 176 NM	6 orbits
MA-9	Orbital	May 15, 1963	G. Cooper	100 NM and 166 NM	22 orbits

* Astrochimp

Appendix E

Gemini Flight Summary

Mission No. & Sequence	Type Mission	Date	Astronauts	Perigee and Apogee (NM)	Mission Duration
1	Orbital unmanned	April 8, 1964		87 and 161	4.25 orbits
2	Ballistic unmanned	January 19, 1965		87 release	1848 NM impact
3	Orbital manned 3 orbits	March 23, 1965	V. Grissom J. Young	87 and 130	Three orbits
IV	Orbital manned 4 days	June 3, 1965	J. McDivitt E. White	87 and 161	long duration 4 days
V	Orbital manned 8 days	August 21, 1965	G. Cooper C. Conrad	87 and 190	long duration 8 days
VI	Orbital manned rendezvous	December 15, 1965	W. Schirra T. Stafford	87 and 146	2 days

VII	Orbital manned 14 days	December 15, 1965	F. Borman J. Lovell	87 and 183	long duration 14 days
VIII	Orbital manned docking	March 16, 1966	N. Armstrong D. Scott	87	½ day
IX	Orbital manned rendezvous	June 3, 1966	T. Stafford E. Cernon	87 and 146	3 days
X	Orbital manned GATV X-S/C rendezvous docking	July 18, 1966	J. W. Young M. Collins	87 and 475	3 days
XI	Orbital manned rendezvous docking	September 12, 1966	C. Conrad P. Gordon	87 and 739	3 days
XII	Orbital manned rendezvous docking	November 11, 1966	J. Lovell E. Aldrin	87 and 151	4 days

Suggested Further Reading

Burgess, Eric. *Satellites & Spacecraft.* New York: MacMillan Co., 1958.

Canby, Courtlandt. *A History of Rockets and Space.* New York: Hawthorn Books, Inc., 1963.

Coombs, Charles. *Rockets, Missiles and Moons.* New York: Morrow & Co., 1957.

Emme, Eugene M. *The History of Rocket Technology.* Detroit: Wayne State University Press, 1964.

Knight, Clayton. *Rockets, Missiles and Satellites.* New York: Grosset & Dunlap, 1958.

Lent, Paul L. *Rockets, Jets and the Atom.* New York: Pen-Ink Publishing Company, 1952.

Ley, Willy. *The Conquest of Space.* New York: The Viking Press, 1949.

Ley, Willy. *Rockets, Missiles, Space Travel.* New York: The Viking Press, rev. ed., 1967.

Pendray, G. Edward. *The Coming Age of Rocket Power.* New York: Harper and Brothers, 1947.

Stine, Harry. *Rocket Power and Space Flight.* New York: Holt & Company, 1957.

Von Braun, Werner, and Ordway, Frederick I. *History of Rocketry & Space Travel.* New York: Thos. Y. Crowell Company, 1966.

Index

earth satellites, 47, 176; early U.S.
research on, 46-47; orbiting of,
47-49, 52-53; launching vehicles for, 49-56, 57-69
Edwards Air Force Base (California), 92
Enos, 140
Explorer satellites, 52-53

flame deflector, 122
Flight Director, 128
fluorine, 64

Gemini program, 73, 120, 126,
127, 134, 141-144, 151
General H. H. Arnold, 131, 132
German scientists, 32, 33
Germany, pioneer rocket work in,
29-31
Glenn, John, 141, 163, 164
Goddard, Dr. Robert, 25, 27, 28,
35, 44, 80
gravity, 74, 75, 76, 77, 139, 162,
176
Greeks, theory of the universe, 15
Grissom, Virgil L., 141, 142, 156
ground tracking, *see* Saturn V,
tracking of
gyroscope, 27

Ham, 140
Huntsville (Alabama), 105, 106,
110

IBM Corporation, 105
Intercontinental Ballistic Missile
(ICBM), 43, 44, 45
Intermediate Range Ballistic Mis-
sile (IRBM), 42, 43
International Geophysical Year,
49

Juno I, 52, 53, 57
Juno II, 53, 57
Juno III, 57
Juno V, 58, 59
Jupiter, 175
Jupiter C rocket, 40-41, 42, 49,
53, 57, 58

Kennedy, John F., 141
Kennedy Space Center, *see* Cape
Kennedy

Launch Complex, 39, 115, 117,
120, 125, 126
Launch Control Center (LCC),
see Launch Complex, 39
launch pad, 122
Liberty Bell, 7, 141
Lindbergh, Charles, 164
liquid engines, *see* rockets, liquid
engine
liquid hydrogen, 60, 88, 124
liquid oxygen, 10, 26, 60, 124
liquid propellants, *see* rockets, liquid propellants
lunar module, *see* Apollo spacecraft, lunar module
Lunar Orbiter, 18

McDonnell Company, 141, 142
McDonnell Douglas Space Sys-
tems Center, 94, 103
Manned Spacecraft Center(Hous-
ton), 128
Manned Space Flight Network
(MSFN), 130
man-rating, *see* Saturn V, man-
rating of
Mars, 150, 175
Marshall Space Flight Center